YOR
ROCKS AND
LANDSCAPE

A FIELD GUIDE

YORKSHIRE GEOLOGICAL SOCIETY

•

EDITED BY COLIN SCRUTTON

Ellenbank
Press

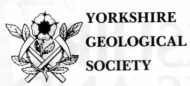

YORKSHIRE
GEOLOGICAL
SOCIETY

The objectives of the Yorkshire Geological Society are to extend the knowledge of the science of geology and to promote and record the results of geological research, with particular emphasis on the North of England.

The Society publishes a journal, the *Proceedings of the Yorkshire Geological Society*, devoted to original work on geology and geomorphology with the emphasis on northern England. A Circular is distributed about six times a year to publicise the winter programme of lectures, the summer field meetings and various other matters of interest to members.

No qualifications are required for membership and there is no entry fee. For further information on the Society and a Membership Application Form, please write to:

John Varker, General Secretary,
Department of Earth Sciences, The University,
Leeds, LS2 9JT.

Also in this series:
Lakeland Rocks and Landscape

Published by Ellenbank Press, The Lathes
Selby Terrace, Maryport, Cumbria CA15 6LX

First published 1994

Typeset in Linotron Baskerville by Deltatype Ltd,
Ellesmere Port, Cheshire
Printed and bound by Athenaeum Press Ltd,
Newcastle upon Tyne

British Library Cataloguing in Publication Data
A catalogue record for this book is available from
the British Library

ISBN 1 873551 08 8

Contents

Preface   5
Introduction   6
Geological history of Yorkshire *Colin Scrutton*   9

FIELD EXCURSIONS

Lower Palaeozoic, Carboniferous and Quaternary

WEST AND NORTH

 1 Lower Palaeozoic rocks of the Craven Inliers *Eric Johnson**   21
 2 The Craven Fault Zone – Malham to Settle *David Mundy
   and Russell Arthurton**   30
 3 Quaternary geology and geomorphology of the area around
   Kisdon, upper Swaledale *James Rose*   42
 4 The North Swaledale Mineral Belt around Gunnerside
   Dick Ineson and Brian Young*   51
 5 The Carboniferous rocks of upper Nidderdale *Albert Wilson*   58
 6 Dinantian and Namurian rocks of Bolton Abbey and
   Trollers Gill *W. John Varker*   66
 7 The Millstone Grit of Almscliff Crag and Harlow Car,
   near Harrogate *Ian Chisholm**   76

SOUTH

 8 The Carboniferous (Namurian and Westphalian) of the
   Cliviger Valley, Todmorden *Paul Wignall and Paul Kabrna*   84
 9 The Upper Carboniferous of the Halifax area *Brian Turner*   92
10 Middle and Upper Carboniferous rocks (Millstone Grit
   and Coal Measures) of the Sheffield region *Mike Romano
   and Martin Whyte*   101

Post-Carboniferous and Quaternary

INLAND

11 The Jurassic, Tertiary and Quaternary around Great Ayton
   and Roseberry Topping, Cleveland Hills *John Senior and
   Jim Rose*   110
12 The Quaternary features of Scugdale, northwest Cleveland
   Hills *Donald Frost**   119

Contents

13 The Permian and Carboniferous rocks of Knaresborough
   Anthony Cooper*   124
14 The Permian rocks of south-central Yorkshire *Denys Smith*   133
15 Jurassic and Cretaceous rocks of the Market Weighton area
   Felix Witham   142

COAST

16 The Lower Jurassic rocks between Staithes and Port
   Mulgrave *Colin Scrutton*   150
17 Lower–Middle Jurassic sequences between Whitby and
   Saltwick *Martin Whyte and Mike Romano*   158
18 Lower and Middle Jurassic rocks between Robin Hood's
   Bay and Hawsker Bottoms *John Senior*   165
19 The Middle–Upper Jurassic sequence between Cayton Bay
   and Yons Nab *Martin Whyte and Mike Romano*   174
20 Jurassic, Cretaceous and Quaternary rocks of Filey Bay
   and Speeton *John Neale and John Catt*   183
21 The Chalk of Flamborough Head *Richard Myerscough*   192

Geology in Yorkshire's museums *Paul Ensom*   200
Glossary   206
Bibliography   216
Index   219

*Officers of the British Geological Survey publish with the permission of the Director.

Preface

This field guide is written and edited exclusively by members of the Yorkshire Geological Society. The Society has a long and distinguished history, having been founded in 1837. From small beginnings among amateurs with an interest in Yorkshire geology, it has grown to have influence well beyond the boundaries of the county and a membership of over 1000 from all over the world. It brings together professional geologists of all descriptions, from universities, surveys and companies, together with amateur geologists who still form a significant proportion of our membership. The Society publishes a prestigious journal, the *Proceedings*, which has a major part of its original papers based on Yorkshire geology.

The original aims of the Society are still observed in the lecture meetings held approximately once a month from October to March, and particularly in the programme of field excursions in the spring and summer months. The lectures are a mixture of original work, mainly on the geology of Yorkshire and northern England, and general reviews, often of much wider scope. Field excursions range all over the county and its near neighbours and offer an opportunity to demonstrate new observations and interpretations of the geology and geomorphology.

Many of you using this guide may already be members of the Yorkshire Geological Society. If you are not, and would like to know more about this fascinating subject, and particularly its development in Yorkshire and the surrounding area, why don't you join us? We would be pleased to welcome you.

Dick Ineson, President, Yorkshire Geological Society

Introduction

In the choice of excursions, an attempt has been made to provide a broad coverage of Yorkshire both geographically and geologically. Whichever part of the county you are in, we hope there will be something to interest you. However Yorkshire is a large place (defined here on its pre-1976 boundary), and to keep this book to a comfortable size a selection has had to be made from among its many sites of geological interest.

An introductory chapter outlines the geological history of the Yorkshire area, providing a framework for the details of the local geology. Each excursion begins with general information on the geology and/or geomorphology covered in the itinerary. Brief notes cover access, parking and walking distances, together with lists of useful Ordnance Survey (O.S.) and British Geological Survey (B.G.S.) maps. In many excursions the background information or itinerary includes notes on the historical exploitation of geological resources, and on other related matters. A section towards the end of the book lists museums in Yorkshire that have geological displays or collections.

All excursions have certain basic requirements for both safety and enjoyment. These include stout shoes or walking boots, sensible clothes and appropriate maps. On higher ground, it may be much colder and more windy than in the valleys, and low cloud may not just spoil appreciation of geological and geomorphological views of the landscape, but may present a danger if you become lost. On foreshores, wellington boots may be a suitable alternative but, whatever your footwear, wet rocks can be very slippery.

For more specific dangers, notes are given in the introductions to the relevant excursions. However it is worth repeating some general points. In locations near quarry or cliff faces, a safety helmet should be worn. Always look at the state of steep faces and, if in doubt about their safety, do not approach them. When using a hammer, it is advisable to wear safety goggles and to make sure that fragments you chip off do not hit other people. In any coastal situation, the state of the tide may be crucial, not only to your view of the geology but to your safety. Always check on the time of low tide and do not start an excursion on a rising tide where access to and from the foreshore is limited.

Some excursions include visits to Sites of Special Scientific Interest.

These are designated not only to conserve our geological heritage but also to protect other features such as the flora. Please observe any specific requests not to hammer rocks or collect fossils.

As far as possible, excursion routes follow public rights of way and keep to open land or the foreshore. Where localities are on private land, permission for access should be sought *beforehand*. We have given as much information as possible to facilitate this. In general, observe the Countryside Code and avoid damage to walls, gates or property. The Geologists Association have published a Code for Geological Field Work, which outlines good practice in the field and can be obtained from the Librarian, The Geologists Association, Department of Geological Sciences, University College, Gower Street, London WC1E 6BT.

We hope that anyone with an interest in geology and geomor-phology will be able to follow the excursions in this guide. However the technical level does vary from one to another, depending on the character of the rocks and the complexity of the area. As an aid, a limited number of technical terms are highlighted in **bold** where first used in each Section and are briefly defined in a Glossary at the end of the book. For more information on any term, or for terms not covered in the Glossary, reference should be made to a geological dictionary (see Bibliography). Bibliographic entries are placed towards the end of the book and are mainly general works. A very few more specific references are included where these have value for a particular excursion.

Finally, I would like to thank all those who have helped me in the compilation of this guide, my colleagues on the Council of the Society for their advice, and the authors for their contributions.

Colin Scrutton, University of Durham

Note

The details of routes given in this guide do not imply a right of way. Users of this guide are responsible for seeking permission where necessary to use footpaths and for access to any private land.

Every effort has been made to ensure that the information in this book is accurate and up-to-date. However, information on any changes to footpaths or exposures, or on threats to any S.S.S.I., would be welcomed by the Society.

Notes on safety have been included but it is the responsibility of the user to take all necessary precautions for their own safety and that of third parties. The publishers and the Society take no responsibility for any accident or injury sustained on any of these excursions.

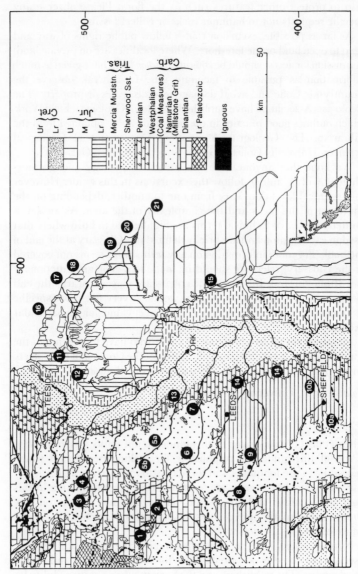

Figure 1 Pre-Quaternary geological map of Yorkshire and adjoining areas showing the location of excursions.

Cret.
- Ur
- Lr

Jur.
- U
- M
- Lr

Trias.
- Mercia Mudstn.
- Sherwood Sst.

Permian

Carb.
- Westphalian (Coal Measures)
- Namurian (Millstone Grit)
- Dinantian

Lr Palaeozoic

Igneous

0   km   50

Geological history of Yorkshire

Colin Scrutton *University of Durham*

The solid geology of Yorkshire is dominated by rocks of the Carboniferous to Cretaceous systems (Fig. 1). The hills and dales of the Pennines in the west, together with the industrial cities of the centre and south, are underlain by Carboniferous rocks. These continue at depth where a narrow belt of Permian scarps and broader Triassic vales stretch south from Teeside and bisect the county. To the east, the deeply dissected tableland of the North York Moors is formed of Jurassic rocks and the rolling wolds to the south lie on the Cretaceous. The effects of the last glaciation are widely apparent in the moulding of landforms, and a veneer of glacial and periglacial sediments obscures much of the solid geology, particularly in the lowlands. Much older rocks, forming the foundation of the county at depth, are exposed at the surface only locally in the far west, where they extend the geological record back to the early Ordovician (Fig. 2). The rocks of the county contain a wide range of economic resources, from lead and zinc to iron and coal, which have been exploited from at least Roman times to the present day. The scars of their extraction are widespread in the countryside and their importance to Yorkshire's historical development is evident in the industrial base of the major centres of population.

At the beginning of this geological history, the area of the British Isles existed as the pieces of a giant jigsaw moving slowly towards their final assembly. In the early–mid Ordovician, the area that is now Yorkshire occupied the northern margin of the micro-continent of Eastern Avalonia, which lay in high southern latitudes (Fig. 3a). During the Ordovician and early Silurian, Eastern Avalonia drifted northwards towards the mid-latitude continent of Baltica, consisting of the landmass from Scandinavia to the Urals, and the large equatorial continent of Laurentia, comprising present-day North

9

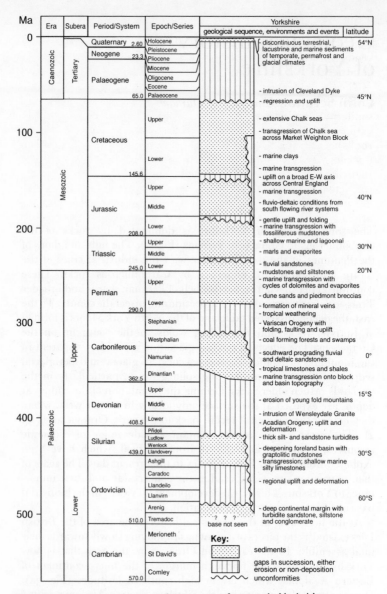

The following table represents the content of the geological column figure:

Ma	Era	Subera	Period/System	Epoch/Series	Yorkshire geological sequence, environments and events	latitude
0	Caenozoic	Tertiary	Quaternary 2.60	Holocene	- discontinuous terrestrial, lacustrine and marine sediments of temperate, permafrost and glacial climates	54°N
				Pleistocene		
			Neogene 23.3	Pliocene		
				Miocene		
			Palaeogene	Oligocene		
				Eocene	- intrusion of Cleveland Dyke	
			65.0	Palaeocene	- regression and uplift	45°N
100	Mesozoic		Cretaceous	Upper	- extensive Chalk seas	
					- transgression of Chalk sea across Market Weighton Block	
				Lower	- marine clays	
			145.6		- marine transgression	
			Jurassic	Upper	- uplift on a broad E-W axis across Central England	
					- marine transgression	40°N
				Middle	- fluvio-deltaic conditions from south flowing river systems	
200			208.0	Lower	- gentle uplift and folding	
					- marine transgression with fossiliferous mudstones	
			Triassic	Upper	- shallow marine and lagoonal	30°N
				Middle	- marls and evaporites	
			245.0	Lower	- fluvial sandstones	20°N
			Permian	Upper	- mudstones and siltstones	
					- marine transgression with cycles of dolomites and evaporites	
			290.0	Lower	- dune sands and piedmont breccias	
					- formation of mineral veins	
300	Palaeozoic	Upper	Carboniferous	Stephanian	- tropical weathering	
					- Variscan Orogeny with folding, faulting and uplift	
				Westphalian	- coal forming forests and swamps	
				Namurian	- southward prograding fluvial and deltaic sandstones	0°
			362.5	Dinantian [1]	- tropical limestones and shales	
					- marine transgression onto block and basin topography	
			Devonian	Upper	- erosion of young fold mountains	15°S
400				Middle		
			408.5	Lower	- intrusion of Wensleydale Granite	
					- Acadian Orogeny; uplift and deformation	
		Lower	Silurian	Přídolí	- thick silt- and sandstone turbidites	
				Ludlow		
				Wenlock	- deepening foreland basin with graptolitic mudstones	30°S
			439.0	Llandovery		
				Ashgill	- transgression; shallow marine silty limestones	
			Ordovician	Caradoc	- regional uplift and deformation	
				Llandeilo		
				Llanvirn		60°S
				Arenig	- deep continental margin with turbidite sandstone, siltstone and conglomerate	
500			510.0	Tremadoc	? ? ? base not seen	
			Cambrian	Merioneth		
				St David's		
			570.0	Comley		

Key:
- sediments
- gaps in succession, either erosion or non-deposition
- unconformities

Figure 2 Geological column and sequence of events in Yorkshire. **Epochs/Series** are shown as of equal length within **Periods/System** for convenience. [1]The term Dinantian no longer has formal status but is retained here for convenience.

America, Greenland, Scotland and northeast Ireland, as the inter-vening Iapetus Ocean and Tornquist's Sea gradually narrowed by the **subduction** of ocean crust.

The Ordovician to Silurian sedimentary sequence, now exposed in the **inliers** along the Craven **Fault** Belt near Settle (Excursion 1), has similarities with that of the Lake District. **Turbiditic** sandstones, with interbedded siltstone, conglomerate and mudstone (see **clastic rocks**) of probable Arenig age are possibly several kilometres in total thickness. They were tightly **folded**, uplifted and eroded in the late Llanvirn–mid-Caradoc interval when a subaerial volcanic island arc was active on the northern margin of Eastern Avalonia, parts of which are preserved in the Lake District. Subsequent crustal extension produced a foreland basin, resulting in the return of marine conditions with a **transgression** in the late Caradoc–Ashgill. Shallow water, mixed clastic–**carbonate rocks** 450 m thick, which are locally richly fossiliferous, were deposited in the late Ordovician. In the Silurian, 35 m of **graptolitic** mudstones and siltstones were laid down in the Llandovery as the seas deepened. The infilling of the foreland basin, the remnant seaway between Laurentia and Avalonia, occurred in the Wenlock and Ludlow, with a 1600 m thick succession of mainly turbiditic sandstones and siltstones.

The collision between Eastern Avalonia, Laurentia and Baltica culminated in the compression and deformation of the Lower Palaeozoic rocks of Northern England in early Devonian times. The Acadian Orogeny, the terminal phase of the **Caledonian Orogenic cycle**, formed a continental area of fold mountains and rugged uplands striking northeast-southwest across most of the area that is now the British Isles. Granite **magmas** were generated at depth during the orogeny and injected as **plutons** into the deformed sedimentary pile. No granites crop out at the surface in Yorkshire, but the Wensleydale Granite and a probable granite under Market Weighton have been detected at depth by geophysical survey. The Wensleydale Granite has been proved by a borehole and dated at 400±10 **Ma**.

The Devonian was a period during which erosional processes removed much of the upland relief and provided great quantities of coarse sediments to **intermontane basins** and to flood plains on the continental margin to the south. However, in the Yorkshire area, no deposits from this period have been proved, and the truncated remnants of the folded Lower Palaeozoic rocks are directly overlain by sediments deposited during the Dinantian (early Carboniferous) marine transgression. This strongly angular **unconformity** can be

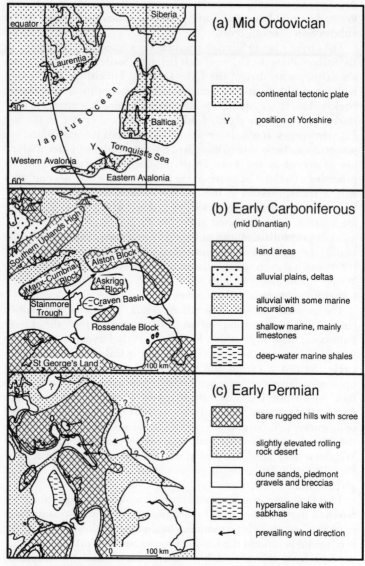

Figure 3 Palaeogeographic maps indicating: (a) the distribution of continental **plates** in the mid Ordovician (based on Scotese & McKerrow 1990) and (b–f) the distribution of land and major sedimentary

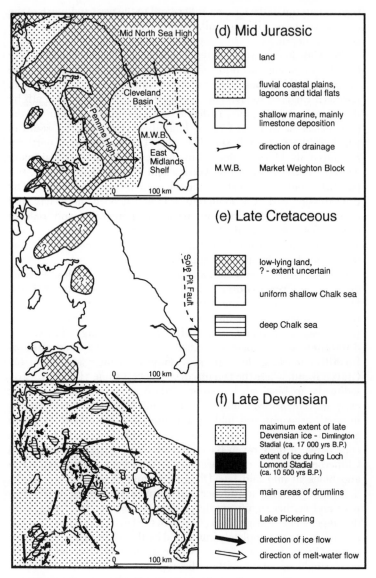

environments at various times in Yorkshire and surrounding areas
(based on Cope, *et al.* 1992 and other sources).

13

seen at outcrop in the Craven Inliers and to the west and north of the county, suggesting that a similar relationship occurs throughout the county at depth.

Post-Caledonian crustal extension broke up the eroded roots of the Caledonian mountains into a series of relatively buoyant blocks and subsiding **half-graben** basins that still influence the topography of northern England today. The Askrigg Block, underlain at depth by the Wensleydale Granite, is defined on its southern margin by the east–southeast trending Craven Fault Belt (Excursion 2), south of which is the Craven Basin (Fig. 3b). The western and northern margins of the block are defined by the Dent Fault and the Stainmore Trough (lying between the Askrigg and Alston Blocks), close and parallel to but mostly just outside the present county boundary. The transgressing early Carboniferous seas first flooded the basins, and locally at the block margins basal conglomerates and reddish sandstones accumulated. As the seas deepened and cleared, shales and limestones of early Dinantian age were deposited in both the Stainmore Trough and Craven Basin.

Carboniferous sedimentation was dominated by cycles of transgression and **regression** on several scales. The six stages of the Dinantian are based on **mesothem** cycles, with calcareous shales and richly fossiliferous, sometimes bituminous limestones characteristic of the transgressive phase, and **oolitic** limestones, **algal** limestones, **dolomites** and in places sandstones, pebble beds and **disconformities** marking the regressive phase in shallow waters. In the Craven Basin, where the Dinantian sequence is some 3 km thick, early sediments are bioclastic limestones and calcareous shales but episodic earth movements from mid-Dinantian into Namurian times resulted in northeast–southwest folding and increased subsidence in which **goniatite**-bearing, deep-water shales predominated. In the transition zone between the Craven Basin and the Askrigg Block, and around Clitheroe, marginal reef limestones were developed between basin and block in mid and late Dinantian times (Excursion 2). In the Stainmore Trough, subsidence and sedimentation more nearly kept pace and neither significant deep water **facies**, nor reef facies, were developed. The Askrigg Block, on which the Dinantian is less than 500 m thick, was not completely inundated by the sea until late Dinantian times (Excursions 2, 5, 6). Minor sedimentary cycles become increasingly apparent within the topmost mesothem, with many repetitions of marine limestone succeeded by shale, sandstone and in places **seatearth** and coal. These are **Yoredale** cycles, a term derived from the old name for Wensleydale, where they are classically developed. The limestone component dominates at lower levels and towards the southern part of the Askrigg Block where open marine conditions prevailed. The clastic sediments increased in proportion in younger cycles and to the north, reflecting the increasing influence of southward **prograding** deltas. The Dinantian limestones are commonly rich in **corals**, **brachiopods** and **foraminifera**, all of which help to date and correlate the sequences.

The Yoredale facies extends up into the Namurian, but from south to north across the county is replaced at progressively younger horizons by the thick and often coarse-grained fluviatile and deltaic sandstones of the Millstone Grit (Excursions 5, 6, 7, 8, 9, 10). By early Namurian times, the clearly defined basin and block topography had largely disappeared, although subsidence rates remained highest, and sedimentary sequences therefore thickest, in the basinal areas. In the Craven Basin, the succession reaches 2.5 km in thickness, in contrast to a mere 370 m on the Askrigg Block and 500 m at Stainmore. These sediments were deposited from river systems flowing predominantly southwestwards into the area. As the deltas advanced, turbidites locally formed on basinal slopes in front of them, over which the deltaic and fluviatile sediments prograded, often building up to sea level to form forested flood plains and swamps. Episodic transgressions of the sea across the delta top resulted in the deposition of thin marine bands with goniatites, vital for dating and correlation.

By Westphalian times, although the cyclicity was undiminished, the marine incursions were fewer and shorter in duration though still widespread. The sandstones were finer grained and thinner and periods of soil formation and swamp vegetation more frequent and prolonged, resulting in thicker coal seams. These Coal Measures (Excursions 8, 9, 10) are now exposed in the Leeds–Sheffield industrial belt of south–central Yorkshire where the sequence is 1500 m thick, and are present in the subsurface to the east. Yorkshire was now part of a broad subsiding area called the Pennine Basin, which in turn was part of a vast belt of tropical Coal Measures sedimentation extending from eastern U.S.A. to Poland. To the south of this was a rising landmass, developing as a result of the **Variscan Orogeny**. Towards the end of the Westphalian, sediments from this landmass caused the infill of the Pennine Basin with cyclic continental red-beds, followed by a period of rather gentle folding, extensive faulting and uplift, particularly in the former basinal areas. For 30 Ma, during the late Carboniferous and early Permian, the resulting upland landscape was deeply weathered and peneplaned in a largely hot, dry climate.

The Carboniferous rocks, principally the Dinantian and Namurian of the Pennines, are host to economic deposits in the form of numerous **mineral veins** (Excursion 4). The principal metalliferous minerals are **galena** and **sphalerite**, with some **chalcopyrite**, **pyrite** and **bornite**, and scattered occurrences of several other minor components. These occur as localized masses or are dispersed in veins in which the main constituent is usually **baryte**, occasionally **witherite** and locally **fluorite**. Mineralization probably occurred in the latest Carboniferous as a result of the circulation of low-temperature hypersaline brines, possibly expelled from the thick sedimentary sequences of the basinal areas (so called Mississippi Valley-type mineralization), through **joint** fracture systems imposed by Variscan earth movements. Vein fractures are widest and cleanest in sandstones and limestones, and locally the latter have been replaced by ores. The Romans certainly mined lead and pre-Roman exploitation has been suggested. The peak of mining activity was in the late 18th and first half of the 19th century, whilst most recently, limited mining activity has concentrated on the former **gangue** minerals baryte and fluorite.

Renewed subsidence in Permian times placed Yorkshire near the western margin of a broad basin extending across northern Europe into Poland, situated in the hot, dry belt about 12–13° north of the equator. Basal and marginal piedmont **breccia** wedges and sheets are associated with patchy continental dune sands of presumed late Lower Permian age (Fig. 3c) (Excursion 14), resting with gentle unconformity on the Carboniferous (Figs. 1, 2). At the beginning of the Upper Permian, the basin, then well below sea level, was flooded, extensively reworking the sands and introducing a period of marine and hypersaline conditions in a fluctuating **epicontinental** sea. Four major cycles of limestones, later altered to dolomites, and succeeding **evaporites**, including **gypsum** (now **anhydrite**), **halite** and potash salts, were developed. These cycles resulted from periodic recharge of the basin by normal marine waters, from which limestones, many oolitic and locally fossiliferous, were formed around the margins. Only the limestones and dolomites are prominent at outcrop in a narrow north–south belt bisecting the county, the evaporites being reduced to thin, silty dissolution residues (Excursions 13, 14). In the first cycle, fossiliferous **bryozoan** and **stromatolitic** patch reefs formed, but in the third cycle the limestones contain only a few plant and invertebrate species. Limestones of the second and fourth cycles do not crop out in Yorkshire but are present in thicker sequences in the subsurface to the east, where potash is mined at Boulby near the coast west-northwest of Whitby. Towards the end of the Permian, continental, water-lain red sandstones, siltstones and mudstones gradually filled the basin from the west.

These continental clastic deposits are unfossiliferous and span the Permo-Triassic boundary, which is consequently difficult to define. In addition, the soft sandstones, **marls** and evaporites of the Triassic, deposited along the western margin of an epicontinental North Sea Basin are rarely seen at outcrop, forming low ground largely mantled by glacial deposits in the Vales of Mowbray and York. The early Triassic (Sherwood Sandstone) consists of fluvial sandstones, with some flood-plain mudstones and siltstones and, in the south of the county, pebble beds deposited by north-flowing river systems. These are overlain with gentle unconformity by a thin concentrate deposit and then by dolomitic and silty mudstones (often red) and evaporites (principally halite) of the Mercia Mudstone, the result of waters from the Tethys Ocean flooding into the North Sea Basin, forming a shallow hypersaline marine environment. Macrofossils are rare but plant spores allow dating and correlation of the lower part of the sequence. Renewed transgression at the end of the Triassic produced thin, shaly mudstones with a **bivalve** fauna, bone beds and argillaceous limestones overlain by soft lagoonal mudstones. The total thickness of Triassic deposits increases from about 400 m at outcrop to some 700 m in the subsurface beneath east Yorkshire.

The late Triassic transgression was the first phase of a major rise in sea level, establishing widespread open marine conditions at the beginning of the Jurassic. In the Yorkshire area, a Cleveland Basin is recognized, bounded to the south by the Market Weighton Block on the northern edge of the East Midlands Shelf (Fig. 3d). Some beds show depositional thinning over the block. However, thinning of Jurassic and early Cretaceous rocks across the Market Weighton area is partly the result of periods of post-depositional erosion, with only the lower part of the Lias being traced continuously across the structure beneath the unconformity at the base of the Chalk (Fig. 1) (Excursion 15). Some important facies changes occur not over the block but to the north of it.

The Lias is a sequence of richly fossiliferous mudstones, calcareous in part, with subsidiary shallow marine sandstones and ironstones of about 420 m maximum thickness in the Cleveland Basin (Excursions 11, 16, 17, 18). **Concretions** are abundant. A cyclic repetition of thin limestones and shales is very evident in the lower part of the succession. In contrast to the two preceding systems, abundant **ammonites** allow a very precise dating and correlation of the

17

sequence. Other fossils include a wide range of bivalves, brachiopods, **belemnites**, less common **echinoderms**, marine reptiles and wood. The ironstones, alum shales and jet were of economic importance historically.

Uplift and gentle folding terminated this marine sequence and the Middle Jurassic consists of about 250 m of fluviatile and deltaic sandstones, siltstones, shales and minor coals with marine intercalations, resting unconformably on various levels of the Lower Jurassic (Excursions 11, 17, 18, 19). These deposits were laid down by south-flowing river systems originating immediately to the north. South of Yorkshire, they pass transitionally into the fully marine sequence of central and southern England (Fig. 3d). Fossils are often common in the marine interbeds and the marshy delta-top environment supported a rich flora which is locally well preserved. A transgression returned fully marine conditions to the area late in the Middle Jurassic. The first sediments deposited were a variety of sandstones, shales and limestones up to 50 m thick, many highly fossiliferous, principally with bivalves and ammonites.

Minor episodes of gentle warping and erosion broke up the Upper Jurassic succession on the Yorkshire coast (Excursions 19, 20), whilst inland and to the south of the county the widely uniform muds of the Oxford Clay became established. This facies only extended to the coast in upper Oxford Clay times where it is 45 m thick. There, it is succeeded by a highly variable 100 m thick complex of limestones, including coral patch-reefs, and fine-grained calcareous sandstones. These too show lateral facies changes north of the Market Weighton area to marine muds typical of much of the eastern Midlands.

Renewed transgression extended marine clay facies back across the Yorkshire area with the deposition of the Kimmeridge Clay, the most laterally persistent and uniform of all late Jurassic sediments and the principal source rock for North Sea oil. Unfortunately the unit is poorly exposed in Yorkshire although in boreholes it may reach about 270 m in thickness. The latest Jurassic and very earliest Cretaceous are not represented in Yorkshire because renewed earth movements resulted in the uplift of an extensive landmass extending from central England into western Europe.

Transgression early in the Cretaceous returned marine conditions to Yorkshire with the deposition of a richly fossiliferous sequence of soft shales and clay some 100 m thick (Excursion 20). The principal fossils are ammonites and belemnites and almost the whole of the lower Cretaceous is represented by this uniform sequence, making it the best and most complete example of this period in the U.K.

Towards the end of early Cretaceous time, the supply of mud ceased and the sea deepened and cleared. This began the period of maximum transgression in the Mesozoic (Fig. 3e), with uniform marine conditions across the whole of western Europe (Excursions 15, 20, 21). Calcareous oozes formed, composed almost wholly of the minute platelets of **coccoliths** (unicellular algae) which abounded in surface waters. Initially, iron oxides stained the oozes and up to 30 m of red **chalk** is recorded in southeast Yorkshire, with varied faunas of **sponges**, bivalves, brachiopods, echinoids, and crinoids. In the late Cretaceous, the red chalk is succeeded by the familiar white chalk which reaches a maximum thickness locally of 500 m. The rock is more marly and harder, due to calcite cementation, than in southern England and **flints** are present between about 40 m and 210 m above the base. The fauna is similar to that of the red chalk, although ammonites are also sporadically found. Distinctive laterally continuous marl and flint layers have proved excellent marker beds for local correlation between sections. The highest parts of the chalk do not crop out in Yorkshire, although they are present in part under the glacial deposits of Holderness.

A major retreat of the sea, together with uplift at the end of the Cretaceous, means that Tertiary sediments may never have been deposited in Yorkshire, although thick sequences are known offshore beneath the North Sea. These earth movements lifted the northwest part of the British Isles and were largely responsible for the prevailing shallow southeasterly tilt of the Mesozoic rocks in eastern and southern Britain. The only undoubted Tertiary rock in the county is the Cleveland **Dyke** (Fig. 1), a **thoeliitic basalt** intrusion up to 25 m wide and a distant representative of the Tertiary igneous complex of Mull. It has been worked almost to exhaustion, mainly for roadstone in a series of quarries from Great Ayton across the Cleveland Hills (Excursion 11).

The most recent geological activity, that of the Quaternary, has had a profound influence on the physiography, superficial deposits and soils of the county (Excursions 3, 11, 12, 20, and briefly elsewhere). The whole area was probably covered by ice sheets on many occasions but the bulk of the evidence relates to the last glacial stage, the Devensian. Glacial and **glaciofluvial** sediments of this age cover northwest Yorkshire and the lowlands of the Vale of York, Teeside and Holderness (Fig. 3f). Elsewhere, periglacial processes redistributed existing superficial sediments as sheets of **gelifluctate** and thin sheets of **loess** across hillside slopes and plateaux, often now mixed in the present topsoil. In the Pennine dales and Cleveland Hills, the effects of glacial meltwater are preserved in the form of channels and outwash deposits. The lowlands of the Vales of Mowbray, York and Pickering, and in Holderness, contain complex associations of **till**, sand and gravel, and laminated lake clays. **Erratics** in these deposits are derived from the Lake District, the Cheviot Hills, Scotland and, in the eastern part of the county, Scandinavia. Locally, interglacial deposits with mammal remains survive in caves, and interglacial shorelines indicate the positions of former high sea levels, similar to that of the present day.

It is only some 17 000 ^{14}C yrs (see **dating**) since the Devensian ice sheet began its retreat from Yorkshire, and the last ice in the northwest Pennine fells disappeared only about 10 500 ^{14}C yrs ago. With post-glacial sea level rise, the county has gradually assumed the familiar form of the present day. This rise is still continuing, albeit very slowly, and coastal erosion in areas such as Holderness, for example, is causing the shoreline to retreat on average by about 1.5 m per year. However we are long past the climatic optimum of the present interglacial and in the distant future (in human terms) the glaciers could return to Yorkshire.

1 · Lower Palaeozoic rocks of the Craven Inliers

Eric Johnson *British Geological Survey, Newcastle upon Tyne*

PURPOSE

To examine the stratigraphy and structure of the Ordovician and Silurian rocks, the Sub-Carboniferous **unconformity**, features of the Pleistocene glaciation, and economic geology.

LOGISTICS

Three half-day excursions, mostly on public rights of way, in the three valleys where Lower Palaeozoic rocks are exposed: Chapel le Dale, Crummack Dale and Ribblesdale. There are car parks, toilets and services in Ingleton, Clapham, Stainforth and Horton in Ribblesdale.

Note Access to Arcow Quarry must be agreed with the quarry manager beforehand (Tel: 0729 860202) and will require safety helmets, protective footwear and insurance cover.

Maps

O.S. 1:50 000 Sheet 98 Wensleydale & Wharfedale; 1:25 000 Outdoor Leisure Map 2, Yorkshire Dales (Western area); B.G.S. 1:63 360 Sheet 50 Hawes; 1:50 000 Sheet 60 Settle.
    B.G.S. Memoir, Settle (Arthurton *et al.*, 1988).

GEOLOGICAL BACKGROUND

The Craven **Inliers** are found on the southern margin of the Askrigg Block, immediately north of the North Craven **Fault** (Fig. 1.1). They provide windows into the Ordovician and Silurian rocks which underlie the western part of the county and probably form the basement at considerable depth elsewhere in Yorkshire. Their

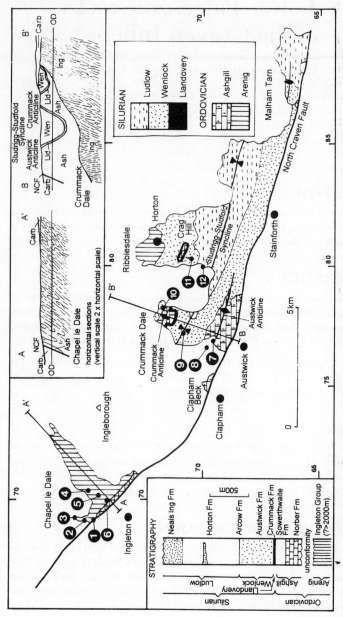

Figure 1.1 Geological map of the Lower Palaeozoic Craven Inliers. Younger, Carboniferous rocks are not ornamented.

deposition, over approximately 200 **Ma**, records the contemporary **plate tectonic** history on the margin of the Eastern Avalonian microcontinent, as it moved north from high southern latitudes, **subducting** Iapetus Ocean crust, before colliding with Baltica and Laurentia (see Fig. 3a for the palaeogeographic terms of this time).

The oldest, Ingleton Group, is probably Arenig in age. The succession of grey-green **turbidite** sandstones, siltstones and **conglomerates** was probably derived from Eastern Avalonia and deposited in a deep marine environment on its northern margin. The group forms part of an arcuate ridge with a distinctive geophysical magnetic signature that extends from Furness in south Cumbria to Norfolk, beneath the cover of younger rocks.

The group was deformed and uplifted as Iapetus Ocean crust began to be subducted during the Llanvirn. By the Llandeilo continued uplift resulted in the **folded** and **cleaved** rocks forming an island arc with subduction related volcanism. Subaerial volcanic rocks are preserved in the Lake District, but no Llandeilo or Caradoc rocks are present in the Craven Inliers.

Subsidence caused the island arc topography to be **transgressed** by an Ashgill sea. The upper Ordovician, a mixed carbonate **clastic** shelf sequence, rests unconformably on the Ingleton Group. Marine conditions persisted throughout the Silurian, with a gradual return to a deep marine environment and the deposition of silty **graptolitic** mudstones.

In the Wenlock, turbidite sandstones (Austwick Formation) derived from Eastern Avalonia entered the basin. Subsidence accelerated in the Ludlow and increasing rates of sedimentation and turbidite sandstones derived from Baltica indicate the near closure of the Iapetus Ocean.

The collision of Eastern Avalonia, Laurentia and Baltica produced folds, cleavage and minor **thrusts** in the early Devonian **Acadian Orogeny**. Granite **plutons**, generated at depth, were emplaced into the deformed sedimentary rocks that formed a continental fold mountain belt during the remainder of the Devonian. Crustal stretching early in the Carboniferous produced a series of rift basins and blocks across the British Isles. The Lower Palaeozoic rocks form part of the buoyant Askrigg Block, underpinned by the Wensleydale Granite. The Craven Faults define the southern margin of the block and separate it from the Craven (rift) Basin. The relief of the continental area gradually declined and subsidence during crustal stretching allowed the tropical Carboniferous seas to slowly transgress across the rifted Lower Palaeozoic terrain.

EXCURSION DETAILS

The stratigraphic names used are those on the Settle 1:50 000 geological map and in the accompanying memoir (Arthurton *et al.*, 1988).

4] 8 / 13

7 / 4 / 9 7

Ingleton, Kingsdale and Chapel le Dale

Begin in the car park on the west side of the River Twiss (SD 693733) and follow the popular Waterfalls walk, a well-laid and maintained footpath. The walking distance is 7 km. The excursion examines the Ingleton Group, the oldest rocks in Yorkshire, the unconformably overlying Carboniferous Limestone and the Craven faults that define the southern margin of the Askrigg Block (Fig 1.1).

The Ingleton Group is a succession of turbidite sandstones and siltstones that have been **isoclinally** folded and suffered low-grade **metamorphism**, probably in the late Llanvirn uplift of the Eastern Avalonia continental margin. The rocks are probably Arenig in age but were formerly considered to be Precambrian because no fossils had been found. Any fossils present initially were destroyed by the metamorphism that gives the rocks their distinctive green colour. The Ingleton Group was eroded prior to the deposition of the Upper Ordovician (Ashgill) sequence.

Locality 1, Swilla Glen. Follow the footpath that leads north from the car park on the alluvial flat that overlies Coal Measures rocks on the downthrow side of the South Craven Fault. The fault is crossed at SD 693737, near the entrance to Swilla Glen, where thick bedded Carboniferous Limestone is exposed in the stream, **dipping** 20° south-southwest. The limestone forms the walls of the glen, the dip decreasing northeastwards into the core of an **anticline**, on the other side of which it dips up to 10° northeast near the North Craven Fault.

The River Twiss follows the fault line for a short distance near Manor Bridge (SD 695745), upstream of which limestone forms the cliffs on the left bank. On the right bank Upper Ordovician calcareous siltstones (Norber Formation) are exposed. About 100 m beyond the bridge the North Craven Fault is exposed on the far bank of the river. An exploratory tunnel for lead mineralization has been driven in the limestone of the **hanging wall**; sheared Norber Formation is present in the **footwall**. Continue upstream to where the Norber Formation–Ingleton Group boundary is crossed before Pecca Bridge. It is unclear whether the boundary is a fault or an unconformity.

Locality 2, Pecca Falls and Quarry. Cross Pecca Bridge (SD 695748) and examine the rocks in the slate quarry. The cleaved siltstone is typical of fine-grained **lithologies** within the Ingleton Group. In the left-hand (southwest) face, sandy laminae indicate subvertical bedding coincident with the cleavage. In the right-hand corner, a slump-fold and its basal dislocation plane reveal that the beds young to the northeast.

At the first viewpoint to Pecca Falls, medium and thick beds of turbidite sandstone are present in the siltstone, marking the gradational passage into the overlying sandstone unit. Near the top of the waterfall, some beds have irregular **sole structures** and a few 0.3–0.4 m thick beds fine upwards with laminated tops. The sedimentary structures confirm that the beds dip and young northeastwards.

A **synclinal** axis is present immediately above the waterfall. A further 60 m along the path thick sandstone beds with laminated tops and siltstone interbeds dip 30–40° southwards and towards Thornton Force the dip gradually steepens.

4/8/13 with Helen

Locality 3, Thornton Force (see cover photograph). The path continues on the Ingleton Group with Carboniferous Limestone a few metres above it on the left. The unconformity represents a time gap of about 150 Ma and is exposed in the waterfall, beneath the limestone overhang. The basal few metres of limestone are sandy and contain layers of Lower Palaeozoic pebbles. The subhorizontal limestone rests on laminated siltstone dipping 70° southeast which passes up into turbidite sandstones, the basal beds forming a ridge in the river, 10 m downstream from the plunge pool.

Continue on the path over limestone via Twisleton Hall towards the River Doe. Exposures of turbidite sandstone are seen near Beezleys.

Locality 4, Beezley Falls. The falls are in subvertical Ingleton Group turbidite sandstones with some interbedded siltstone; the succession youngs southwestwards. Thick bedded sandstones form each cascade, with plunge pools developed on the siltstone units. If the river is not in spate, the beds can be examined in the river bank above the second cascade by scrambling down from the path. There bedding is clearly defined and on polished surfaces sedimentary structures are revealed, e.g. small-scale slump folds in a 0.1 m thick siltstone interbed. Rejoin the main path to the foot of the falls, where the sandstone passes up into siltstone. Baxengill Gorge is cut in isoclinally folded siltstone. A syncline and anticline are crossed on the way to Snow Falls.

Locality 5, Snow Falls. The cleaved siltstones of the Ingleton Group can be examined in the quarry floor between the path and the river. In the southwest quarry face two north–south trending basic **dykes**, 7 to 8 m apart, cut obliquely through the siltstones. The eastern dyke is most obvious; the western one, in the corner of the quarry, is overgrown. The dykes are also exposed in the river at the downstream extremity of the quarry. About 60 m southwest of the quarry, the siltstone passes gradationally upwards into sandstone.

Locality 6, Twisleton Glen. The Ingleton Group sandstone in Twisleton Glen is deformed in an isoclinal syncline. Inverted beds on the southwest limb, dipping 70° southwest, are exposed alongside the footpath between the bridge (SD 702742) and quarry 50 m further downstream. Slump folds are present in a 2–3 m wide zone in the siltstones between the path where it enters the quarry and the river. In the quarry, the planar laminated siltstones are subvertical. South of it, towards the North Craven Fault, the outcrop is **drift** covered.

Continue on the footpath to return to the car park in Ingleton. In Meal Bank Quarry (SD 698737), on the opposite side of the river, there is an impressive section of Carboniferous Limestone that lies between the North and South Craven Faults.

Crummack Dale

Begin at the Crummack and Thwaite Lane crossroad (SD 759692), 300 m north of Austwick Town Head, accessible from either Clapham or Austwick. The walking distance is 7–12 km.

The excursion examines stratigraphy and structure of the Ashgill to Wenlock parts of the Windermere Group, the Sub-Carboniferous unconformity, and effects of the Pleistocene glaciation (Fig. 1.1).

Locality 7, Nappa Scars (SD 768697). The footpath 50 m west of the crossroads leads to Nappa Scars where the Sub-Carboniferous unconformity is exposed. Pebbly limestone and conglomerate **onlap** a palaeocliff in cleaved calcareous siltstone of the Upper Ordovician (Ashgill) Norber Formation. Springs a few metres above the base of the limestone indicate diversion of the groundwater flow by the impermeable Ordovician rocks. Follow the footpath to the stile at SD 768697, cross the wall and scramble down to the base of the cliff to find exposures of the Norber Formation and the unconformity.

The prominent planes in the calcareous siltstone that dip 60–70° south-southwest are the Acadian cleavage. Bedding is ill-defined but a few laminae dip northwards at about 40°. A sparse **brachiopod** and **trilobite** fauna indicates the Rawtheyan Stage of the Ashgill.

The unconformity lies in the undercut part of the cliff. The basal few metres of the Carboniferous consist of clast-supported boulder beds and conglomerate. Many of the larger boulders are Austwick Formation sandstone. This is overlain by matrix-supported conglomerate in which abundant Lower Palaeozoic pebbles and a few reworked Carboniferous limestone clasts are cemented together by a limestone matrix. Higher up, the limestones gradually become pebble-free.

On the cliff top look east-southeast, along the prominent scarp of Norber Brow, an exhumed palaeocliff, its form today closely resembling that in Carboniferous times. The limestones abut and eventually onlap the cliff, indicating the marine transgression onto the irregular topography of the Askrigg Block. Return to the stile at SD 768697 and head for Locality 8.

Locality 8, Norber (SD 767700). The limestone pavement is strewn with blocks of dark Austwick Formation sandstone and laminated siltstone. The blocks were plucked by the ice from outcrops (SD 770704) 1 km to the north in Crummack Dale. The pillars of limestone beneath the **erratics** have been used to gauge the rate of limestone dissolution in post glacial times.

Again return to the stile at SD 768697, take the footpath along Norber Brow and head northwards on Crummack Lane. The source of the erratic blocks can be seen in the small crags on the left-hand side of the lane before the junction at SD 772706. Take the footpath northeastwards to Locality 9.

Locality 9, Central Crummack Dale (SD 773708). Follow the footpath northeast for 250 m, to where it crosses a stream that is coincident with the axis of the Studrigg–Studfold Syncline. Look west-northwest towards the unconformity on the west side of the valley, up the **plunge** direction of the fold; the **strike** of the sandstone beds (Austwick Formation) can be seen to swing round in the fold closure. The erosion-resistant sandstones form a palaeotopographic high point on the Sub-Carboniferous unconformity which has risen more than 100 m from Nappa Scars. About 300 m northeastwards along the footpath, the thick-bedded turbidite sandstones on the northern limb of the syncline can be examined. Towards Austwick Beck (SD 778715), the ground is extensively drift covered, but to the east on Hunterstye, another major fold, the Crummack Anticline, can be seen. Join the lane and continue northwards to Locality 10.

27

Locality 10, Moughton Whetstone Hole (SD 784719). Where the footpath leaves the enclosed farmland is Moughton Whetstone Hole. Adjacent to the stream, the ground is littered with fragments of dark red and green banded rock, the remnants of a bygone enterprise that worked the Austwick Formation sandstone for whet, or sharpening, stones. The dark red and green banding phenomenon, known as liesegang rings, results from the weathering of iron oxides in the sandstone. This occurred during the Devonian and early Carboniferous when the deformed Lower Palaeozoic rocks were part of a continental area and subjected to subaerial erosion. In some fragments laminae (bedding) are preserved, crosscut by the younger liesegang rings. The colour banded rock can be seen *in situ* on Capple Bank, in small exposures north of the footpath, next to the wall.

Return down the lane towards Wharfe. Southward-dipping Austwick Formation can be seen below the unconformity on Studrigg (SD 781708). The axis of the Studrigg–Studfold Syncline is crossed where the lane turns sharply to the right (SD 777705). Northward-dipping rocks can be seen next to the ford in Austwick Beck where Silurian 'flags' have been used to construct a clapper bridge. The lane to Wharfe follows the foot of the escarpment formed by northward-dipping Austwick Formation sandstone. There is a choice of footpaths to return to Austwick and Clapham.

Ribblesdale

Younger parts of the Silurian succession are preserved in Ribblesdale because the main synclinal axis plunges east-southeast.

The stratigraphy, sedimentology and structure of the Wenlock and Ludlow parts of the Windermere Group and the Sub-Carboniferous unconformity are superby exposed in two quarries less than 1 km apart (Fig. 1.1).

Locality 11, Arcow Quarry (SD 802705). Access to the quarry should have been arranged beforehand (see logistics).

The roadstone quarry is in the Austwick, Arcow and Horton Formations on the southward-dipping, northern limb of the Studrigg–Studfold Syncline. The structure is most clearly seen from the east side of the quarry (SD 804705). On the north side there is an east-southeast plunging anticline, a parasitic fold on the limb of the main syncline. The anticline and most of the quarry are in the Austwick Formation, an interbedded succession of turbidite sandstone and siltstone. On the south side of the quarry the overlying Arcow and Horton Formations are present. The succession can be examined in detail on one of the benches part way up the west side of the quarry.

The sandstone units consist of parallel-bedded fine to medium grained turbidites up to 2 m thick. Some of the thicker beds have coarse bases, consisting of ill-sorted quartz, feldspar and rock fragments with a clay matrix. Sole structures, mostly **flute casts**, on the base of some beds indicate turbidity currents flowing from an east-southeast direction. Ripple marks on the top of the sandstones, however, show current reworking from the west-southwest. The sandstones pass gradationally upwards into overlying dark-grey, parallel-laminated siltstones containing a few thin mudstone and siltstone turbidites. Graptolites of Wenlock age are present. Approximately 20 m of siltstone separate the youngest sandstone unit from the overlying Arcow Formation.

The Arcow Formation comprises 9 m of medium to light-grey, weakly bedded, calcareous siltstone. The basal metre is thin bedded and some beds are ripple **cross-laminated**. Extensive **bioturbation** has destroyed most of the bedding. It contains a sparse shelly fauna dominated by **orthocones**. **Benthonic** fauna and bioturbation indicate an oxygenated depositional environment, contrasting with anoxic conditions for the beds above and below. There is a 2 m gradational passage into the overlying Horton Formation.

The Horton Formation consists of dark-grey, parallel-laminated siltstone that is sandy and calcareous in part. Calcareous nodules occur near the base, often in layers. Only the oldest part of the 700 m thick succession, with poorly preserved Ludlow graptolites, is exposed in the quarry.

Locality 15, Combs Quarry, Foredale (SD 800701). Follow the road from Foredale to the terrace of cottages on the hillside above. A path leads to the quarry.

The quarry worked the dark-grey, laminated siltstone of the Horton Formation for flagstones. The siltstones dip steeply south and are lithologically similar to those in Arcow Quarry. Thin interbeds of bentonite (off-white volcanic clay from large, distant, subaerial eruptions) are present in the siltstone succession. They are much softer than the siltstone, forming recesses and prominent bedding planes. The Sub-Carboniferous unconformity is exposed at the top of the quarry face; bedding in the Carboniferous limestone above is subhorizontal.

2 · The Craven Fault Zone – Malham to Settle

David Mundy *Talisman Energy, Calgary* and
Russell Arthurton *British Geological Survey,
Keyworth, Nottingham*

PURPOSE

This excursion observes Carboniferous (Dinantian and Namurian) stratigraphy and structural relations at the southern margin of the Askrigg Block along the line of the Middle Craven **Fault** (MCF) between Malham and Settle. Features relating to mineralization, Quaternary geology and geomorphology will also be addressed.

LOGISTICS

The itinerary covers some 9 km, with an optional side trip to Victoria Cave (*Locality 15*). It may be tackled as a half-day or a full-day walk, starting at Gordale Bridge (SD 913634), or for a shorter walk, from Malham itself (SD 990636). The excursion is entirely within the confines of the Yorkshire Dales National Park; *thus hammering of the exposures is strongly discouraged.*

There is a large pay-and-display car park adjoining the National Park information centre in Malham. There are several car parks in Settle; alternatively, a small number of vehicles can park on the roadside verge adjacent to the last *Locality 18* (SD 836630), thus avoiding a 1.5 km road walk to Settle.

Maps

O.S. 1:50 000 Sheet 98, Wensleydale & Upper Wharfedale; 1:25 000 Outdoor Leisure Map 10, Yorkshire Dales-Southern Area; B.G.S. 1:50 000 Sheet 60, Settle (drift edition recommended for this traverse).

B.G.S. Memoir, Settle (Arthurton *et al.*, 1988).

GEOLOGICAL BACKGROUND

The Carboniferous (Dinantian, Namurian) palaeogeography of the North of England was greatly influenced by structurally controlled

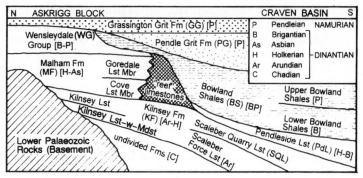

Figure 2.1 Relationships and ages of principal rock units referred to in the itinerary.

blocks of Lower Palaeozoic basement, which under a regime of largely extensional rifting, produced depositional settings of ramp, rimmed shelf and basin. The Craven Faults, and in particular the Middle Craven Fault (MCF), defined the southern margin of the Askrigg Block, a northward-dipping tilt-block of isostatically buoyant (granite-cored) Lower Palaeozoic basement. This block formed a site suitable for shallow water limestone deposition, and contrasted markedly with the subsiding area to the south, where deeper water environments were formed, characterized by both mudstone and limestone deposition.

By late Dinantian times there was a clear differentiation between a rimmed carbonate shelf developed on the Askrigg Block, with marginal carbonate build-ups (the Cracoean 'reef' limestones), and the deeper water settings of the Craven Basin. These build-ups had a unique set of **facies** and supported a prolific invertebrate fauna. The **dip** of the Malham Formation in the **hanging wall** of the MCF is always greater than that on the adjacent **footwall**, and implies northward rotation of the hanging wall. The rotation is a reflection of a concavity in the MCF plane, with the fault plane flattening out with depth; such fault geometries are described as listric. In detail, the Visean (late Dinantian) depositional history of the shelf-edge was complex, and involved syndepositional (extensional) 'growth fault- ing' along the MCF, followed by a major erosive phase instigated by a **strike-slip** component on the Craven faults with localized compres- sional effects. Mudstones of the Bowland Shales progressively covered these disrupted Dinantian limestones, burying the 'reefs' and lapping over the MCF; the Bowland Shales passing up into the siltier and sandier Pendle Grit Formation. After further structural upheaval and erosion, widespread across the Askrigg Block, the deltaic, pebbly, coarse-grained sandstones of the Grassington Grit Formation extended southwards across the Block and into the Craven Basin.

EXCURSION DETAILS

Locality 1, Gordale Scar viewpoint (SD 913634). View from Gordale Bridge or proceed as a side trip into Gordale Scar. The spectacular gorge in the Malham Formation was probably carved as a **meltwater channel** beneath the Devensian ice-sheet. Upstream of the waterfall the gorge dog-legs abruptly to the northeast, where a series of minor extensional faults have controlled the erosive path of the meltwater channel. These faults are exposed just above the **tufa** screen and are part of the complex set of fractures between the North and Middle Craven faults. The superb Malham Formation section in Gordale Scar exposes 43 m of the Cove Limestone Member and 94 m of the overlying Gordale Limestone Member. This location is designated as the stratotype for the latter. The contact of the two formations is a strong bedding plane defining the top of the first persistent scar feature.

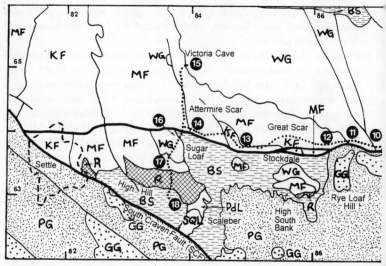

Figure 2.2 Principal geological features between Gordale Scar and Settle. Abbreviations as in Fig. 2.1.

Locality 2, Janet's Foss, Gordale Beck (SD 912633). Take the footpath which leads south from Gordale Lane into Gordale Beck. The footpath enters a wooded valley where the stream is interrupted by a small waterfall (Janet's Foss) below which is a moss-covered tufa screen. This exposure of Gordale Limestone forms the northern part of the hanging wall block of Wedber Brow. These limestones dip east-northeast at 25° towards a fault defining the eastern margin of the Wedber block. The middle and southern parts of Wedber Brow are formed by 'reef' limestones. The small cave known as Janet's Cave was, according to records, inhabited in the late 17th century by smelters working the copper mines at Pikedaw to the west. The exposed Gordale Limestone above the waterfall is notably mottled as a result of the burrowing activities of bottom-dwelling organisms. This burrow-mottling can be seen in exposures in the path on the return to Gordale Lane.

Locality 3, Gordale Lane, at the base of Cawden Hill (SD 904629). View the 'reef' limestones on the southern flank of Cawden from a position just west of the bend in Gordale Lane. These carbonate build-ups, first recognized by R. H. Tiddeman, were largely constructed by organisms, and had depositional topographies of over

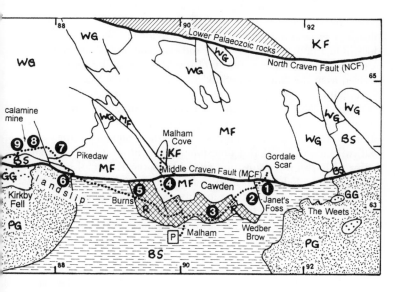

100 m. They are not, however, analogous to present-day coral-algal framework reefs. Three principal subfacies make up the build-ups – *bank*, *flank*, and *framework*. The bank is the poorly bedded core of the build-ups, while the flank facies formed the basin-facing palaeoslope, with depositional dips up to 35°. These subfacies contained a diverse and locally prolific biota dominated by **brachiopods**, **molluscs**, **crinoids**, **bryozoans** and **corals.** The lower southern slope of Cawden here consists largely of flank beds dipping southwards at about 30° (clearly seen in the old quarries just beyond the wall), whilst the middle slopes consist of flank and bank facies. The small raised feature visible at the top of the hill is a good example of the framework facies, which developed locally in the shallowest-water setting of the build-up. The present-day topography on this slope is a reflection of the original profile of the build-up. Proceed to Malham village.

Locality 4 (optional), Malham Cove viewpoint (SD 898633). Follow the road northwards through the village to the footpath gate leading to the Cove. View the geology of this spectacular section from here, or if you have the time and the energy inspect it at closer range. Malham Beck resurges from the base of the cliff. This stream receives only a small component of water from the Malham Tarn 'Water Sinks', a sink at the head of the Watlowes dry valley (which terminates at the Cove), taking the overflow water from Malham Tarn. This water source, although seemingly the obvious candidate for the Cove resurgence, does in fact flow at a deeper level and rises south of Malham as the Airehead Springs. The majority of the Malham Beck resurgence is derived from the 'Smelt Mill Sink' 1.2 km west of the Water Sinks.

Malham Cove is the stratotype of the Cove Limestone which is here 72 m thick. The top of the member is the bedding plane some 5 m above a prominent overhang (compare Gordale Scar). The basal 10 m of the overlying Gordale Limestone forms the remainder of the Cove cliff, with a well-developed limestone pavement on its top. A small **inlier** of dark grey grainstone referable to the Kilnsey Limestone Member of the Kilnsey Formation occurs in the valley bottom below the Cove. While you are at this locality, take the opportunity to view the western side of Cawden, where bedded Malham Formation in the hanging wall of the MCF can be seen dipping northwards at about 20°. Return to Malham.

Locality 5, Burns Barn (Field Barns) (SD 893632). Take the footpath from Malham heading to Field Barns and Pikedaw. The footpath crosses 'reef' limestone belonging to the Malham Formation. Small exposures in this tract show shelly limestones referable to the *bank* subfacies. The contact of the Bowland Shales on the reef limestones occurs 100 m west of Field Barns, and is defined by the rising ground east of Sell Gill. Although both the limestone and Bowland Shales are covered by a veneer of **till**, the ill-drained ground associated with the shales is conspicuous. Proceed westwards, up Pikedaw Gill, picking up the line of the MCF defined by the Malham Formation escarpment of Pikedaw to the north. Review the course of the fault eastwards from Malham.

Locality 6, Pikedaw Gill (SD 882636). The stream runs close to the margin of an extensive landslip, involving the Namurian formations to the south. Stop at the portal of the Pikedaw lead level beside the footpath. The portal has a stone-built arch with a keystone dated 1872, and is one of several entrances to the mine workings exploiting **galena**-bearing **veins** of the Pikedaw area. Most of the lead veins trend northwest–southeast, coincident with the general fault trend between the NCF and MCF. The Pikedaw area has a long history of mining probably dating from the 17th century, with copper, zinc and lead minerals extracted.

Locality 7, Pikedaw (SD 881638). Follow the footpath 200 m northeast of Locality 6 to limestone exposures bordering the footpath. Here the Gordale Limestone, close to the contact of the Hawes Limestone, is partially silicified. Brown **quartz**-rock has replaced limestone in irregular zones which stand proud of the limestone surface due to their greater resistance to weathering. Analogous silicified limestone forms northwest-trending replacement zones within the Hawes Limestone just to the north. These replacement bodies, clearly visible east of the footpath, weather as raised ribs carrying a more acid-tolerant flora than the limestone. The landslip on the eastern slopes of Kirkby Fell is well seen from here. The failure occurred in two episodes, each post-dating the Devensian glaciation, with the Pendle Grit Formation and the lower leaf of the overlying Grassington Grit Formation collapsing to leave jumbled debris extending downslope onto the Bowland Shales.

Locality 8, Calamine Mine 'New Shaft' (SD 876640). A concrete cap with a metal door covers a 21 m deep shaft, dug in 1806 for access to the mine, which yielded **smithsonite** (calamine) from a Quaternary cavern system some 70 m in length. The mineral occurs as a sediment flooring the caverns, and was discovered during copper mining in

1788. The calamine was originally brought to surface via the difficult access of the copper mine to the west (see Locality 9). The New Shaft (rediscovered in 1944) was constructed to ease the handling of the mineral. It is estimated that up to 5000 tons of calamine, used largely in brass-making, were extracted before the mine was closed in 1830.

Locality 9, Pikedaw Head Gate (SD 875630). Proceed westward from the New Shaft through the gate in the wall. The disturbed ground immediately west of the wall is the result of copper workings and consists of shafts, bell-pits and their spoil. The copper deposits were in poorly differentiated veins and impregnations and were very difficult to work. The heap of limestone debris to the west of the gate is that from the 'principal copper shaft', and it was by this exit that calamine was initially brought to surface. Continuing westwards, observe the ground to the south (eg 200 m west of Locality 9). Here a line of shake holes defines the contact of the Upper Bowland Shales on the Hawes Limestone. The Namurian shales **overlap** an eroded limestone surface north of the MCF, a manifestation of a substantial **throw** in the MCF and subsequent erosion of the footwall scarp before the deposition of the shales. This buried fault-scarp is an example of the pre-Namurian topography.

Locality 10, Kirkby Fell viewpoint (SD 870639). The MCF crops out about 100 m south of the path, the rising ground of Kirkby Fell beyond being Pendle Grit Formation capped by Grassington Grit. To the southwest, two leaves of Grassington Grit form the prominent Rye Loaf Hill. To the west the path descends and crosses a narrow north-northwest-trending dry valley, developed along another of the subsidiary extensional faults which cross the ground between the MCF and NCF. This subsidiary fault is linked with several others to the north, forming a complex zone of westward down-stepped slices. Silicified limestone analogous to that seen at Locality 7 is exposed adjacent to the path, and a line of small mineral workings follows the fault. Spoils have yielded **sphalerite**, galena, **malachite**, **azurite** and **baryte**.

Locality 11, Great Scar viewpoint (SD 866639). Continue westwards for some 400 m. The slopes and gullies to the northwest display the stratigraphy of the lower part of the Wensleydale Group (formerly called the Yoredales). This succession represents a continuation of shelf carbonate deposition, but with periodic interruption by mudstones in this area, but mudstones and sandstones (some with coals) north of the NCF. These **siliciclastics** were deposited during the southward **progradation** of a deltaic complex.

Compared with the underlying Malham Formation, the Wensleydale Group limestones are typically darker grey and contain more visually conspicuous fossils (particularly crinoids, corals, brachiopods and **algae**). The Wensleydale Group section exposed in the Great Scar escarpment includes, in ascending order, the Hawes Limestone (27 m), Gayle Limestone (16 m) and Hardraw Scar Limestone (14 m); the latter forming the skyline. The stepped topography is controlled by the mudstone bands separating the limestones. The top of the Lower Hawes Limestone contains several prominent fossil markers including algal (**oncolite**) beds ('*Girvanella* Band'), a *Gigantoproductus* brachiopod bed, and a coral **biostrome** dominated by colonies of *Siphonodendron* and *Lithostrotion*.

Locality 12, Stockdale viewpoint (SD 863639). Follow the footpath to the head of Stockdale. The Gordale Limestone produces continuous scars in the footwall fault scarp of the MCF. The position of the contact with the underlying Cove Limestone Member, on the top of the lowest scar-former, is cleary discernible and analogous to that at Malham. Northwest-trending fractures of little throw have influenced erosion, producing nicks in the escarpment. The MCF runs south of the whale-back ridge in the valley bottom. The ridge is defined to the north by the more northerly of two westerly-diverging fractures which here characterize the MCF; the other fracture, with most of the throw, occurs some 100 m to the south, concealed by Bowland Shales.

High South Bank, south of the main valley, is an inlier of Dinantian limestones forming a northward-dipping hanging wall dip-slope. This inlier is analogous to that at Malham, and is almost certainly fault-defined on its eastern and western margins. Bowland Shales are banked against the limestone. Prior to burial by these mudstones, the limestone of this hanging wall block had undergone significant erosion. A small outcrop of 'reef' limestones forms the southernmost part of the inlier (on the skyline), while the main dip-slope (locally dipping up to 30°) is formed of Malham Formation and Wensleydale Group. The latter includes the Hawes to Hardraw Scar limestones, but these have been attenuated to a 5 m interval, and contain **conglomeratic** units. Quarries on the northern end of the inlier expose **cross-bedded** grainstones, correlatives of the Middle Limestone (Brigantian) of Fountains Fell. Small mineral workings occur in the Wensleydale Group limestones, with galena, malachite and baryte in the spoils, while a large area of quartz-rock has replaced the

Malham Formation. Attenuation of the early Wensleydale Group limestones and succeeding erosion of the shelf margin, suggests a slight compressional regime on the previously extensional fault line (a process known as fault inversion) before collapse of the hanging wall into a series of downthrown fault-blocks in late Dinantian times. The subsidiary faults (mostly northwest-trending) both north and south of the MCF were formed at this time, and reflect a component of right-lateral movement on the Craven fault system.

Locality 13, Stockdale Lane corner (SD 848638). Proceed westward to Stockdale Lane, then to the footpath gate at the bend in the lane 500 m ahead. The viewpoint, immediately north of the MCF, gives a good perspective of the High Hill hanging wall block relative to the Malham Formation footwall escarpment that includes Attermire Scar. The High Hill fault block contains 'reef' limestone exposures on the southern scarp-face and Malham Formation with overlying Wensleydale Group on the main dip slope, with dips from $15°$ to $25°$ towards the MCF. The throw on the fault using the datum of the base of the Hawes Limestone is calculated to be of the order of 170 m, much less than at Stockdale, but analogous to that at Wedber Brow, Malham. The High Hill block is truncated on its eastern margin by a fault, with Bowland Shales forming the low, poorly drained ground on the downside. The trace of this fault is not, however, shown on the B.G.S. map because the Bowland Shales overlap the fault plane (i.e. the fault is pre-Bowland Shales). This relationship clearly demonstrates the separation into blocks of the hanging wall geology by the subsidiary faults south of the MCF and also demonstrates the variation of throw of these isolated fault blocks relative to the main fault. The small roadside exposures near this viewpoint are dark grey grainstones of the Kilnsey Limestone. These are the oldest Dinantian rocks observed on this excursion; they crop out along the base of the slope (Little Banks), but are truncated by a fault east of Attermire Scar.

Locality 14, Attermire Scar – Warrendale Knotts viewpoint (SD 840641). Follow the footpath westward to the gate in the wall below Attermire Scar. The Malham Formation produces magnificent exposures in the fault scarp of the MCF. This escarpment is cut by northwest-trending faults which have produced zones of weakness along which narrow gullies have been eroded. These faults are part of the complex of minor fractures of very late Dinantian age which characterizes the ground between the NCF and MCF. As at Pikedaw and near Kirkby Fell, some are mineralized.

Locality 15 (optional), Victoria Cave (SD 838650). Take the footpath between Attermire Scar and Warrendale Knotts northwards for some 850 m. En route consider the fault-controlled topography to the west. The fault bordering Langcliffe Scars has a throw of up to 90 m. Climb the scree-strewn slope to the entrance of Victoria Cave. The cliff gives an opportunity for viewing the Gordale Limestone at close quarters. Four emergent (palaeokarstic) surfaces occur over a 17 m section of the cliff. The cave is an important site for cave archaeology and Pleistocene geology. Discovered in 1837 (the year of Queen Victoria's coronation) the cave was excavated intermittently over many years, but a major excavation was carried out between 1870 and 1878. Two distinct cave earths were found. The 'Upper' contained Neolithic cultural remains with Romano-British artifacts scattered on the surface, and the 'Lower', separated by a laminated clay and truncated by till at the mouth of the cave, was a Last Interglacial (Ipswichian) bone bed with the remains of nine large mammals including brown bear, spotted hyaena, lion, hippopotamus and narrow-nosed rhinoceros, indicating a use alternating between hyaena den and bear cave. Calcite speleothems enclosing the bones have been dated using the ^{230}Th/^{234}U method and give an age for the fauna in the cave vicinity at or just before 120 000 ($\pm$ 6000) yrs BP. Return to Locality 14.

Locality 16, Sugar Loaf Hill (SD 836638). Cross the wall and continue east for 100 m to steps providing access to the footpath leading to Sugar Loaf Hill, in the High Hill fault block. Proceed 350 m southwards to the base of the conical shaped Sugar Loaf Hill. The dark grey limestones dipping at 18° immediately to the west are Lower Hawes Limestone. The base of this limestone provides a reliable datum on which the throw of the MCF can be calculated (here 170 m). Please note that this area of Hawes Limestone has been inadvertently shaded as Cove Limestone on the solid edition of the Settle 1:50 000 geological map, but corrected on the drift edition. The strata forming Sugar Loaf Hill are early Namurian (Pendleian) in age and **unconformably** overlie the limestones of the lower part of the Wensleydale Group. Most of the hill is composed of intercalated mudstone, siltstone and thin cherty limestone (30 m in all), collectively named the Sugar Loaf Shales, while the top of the hill is capped by 5 m of shelly (brachiopod) wackestone, the lower third of the Sugar Loaf Limestone. The local names reflect the unique character of these units, which are correlatives of the nearby Upper Bowland Shales, but more analogous in lithology to the Namurian part of the Wensleydale

Group (the Main Limestone and underlying siltstones as found, for example, on Fountains Fell). The Sugar Loaf succession represents the localized deposition of a late Wensleydale Group facies on an isolated fault block, when the adjacent tract was typically characterized by the deeper water deposits of Bowland Shales. These stratigraphic relations indicate the relative independence and variable subsidence rates of the isolated blocks forming the hanging wall of the MCF.

Locality 17, High Hill, eastern side (SD 837634). Continue southwards for a further 300 m to where the footpath runs close to the wall, following the line of a northwest-trending subsidiary fault, to the west of which are large replacive **dolostone** bodies in the Gordale Limestone. Observe the Gordale Limestone immediately to the west where well-bedded limestones are dipping at about 15°. Proceed southwards to the remains of a limekiln just west of the path. The quarried limestone section adjacent to the kiln exposes unbedded bank facies of the marginal 'reef' limestones. Notice that the bedded Gordale Limestone (previously viewed) overlaps these 'reef' limestones. The Gordale Limestone in this vicinity thus formed at the very edge of the original shelf, and would have passed into or lapped onto the marginal build-ups somewhere out of the exposure to the south; the present juxtaposition of beds reflecting erosion on the front of the shelf margin build-up.

Locality 18, Corner of High Hill Lane and Stockdale Lane (SD 836630). From this location, view the steep southern slope of High Hill, formed in 'reef' limestones. This topography is a pre-Namurian surface exhumed from a cover of Upper Bowland Shales, and gives an impression of the original bathymetry of the shelf margin. The extensive late Dinantian erosion on the front of the build-up has all but

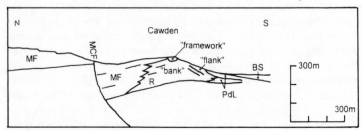

Figure 2.3 Geological section across the Middle Craven Fault near Malham. Abbreviations as in Fig. 2.1.

removed the basinward-dipping flank beds (as seen at Cawden, Malham), revealing mostly the unbedded 'core' of bank facies. Debris from this erosional episode was deposited to the south as conglomerates and boulder beds of the Pendleside Limestone and Lower Bowland Shales (as exposed nearby at Scaleber). This erosion surface has cut down progressively southwards, through the northward-dipping succession in the fault block defined by the South Craven Fault, intercepting the pre-'reefal' Holkerian and Arundian succession of the Scaleber Quarry and Scaleber Force limestones (correlatives of the Kilnsey Formation). This deep erosion on the downside of the MCF (well exposed at Scaleber Beck and Scaleber Force some 600 m to the southwest) is associated with the minor compressional episode that preceded the major collapse on the faults. Continue west back to Settle via High Hill Lane (1.5 km) or rejoin vehicles parked adjacent to this locality.

3 · Quaternary geology and geomorphology of the area around Kisdon, upper Swaledale

James Rose *Royal Holloway, University of London*

PURPOSE

To examine landforms and sediments in the valleys and on the valley-side slopes around Kisdon, upper Swaledale, to demonstrate the effects of: (i) glaciation and glacier wastage during the Dimlington **Stadial** of the Late Devensian (ii) **paraglacial** readjustment of the glacial landscape by fluvial and slope-forming processes during the Devensian Lateglacial and Holocene and (iii) the effects of 19th-century mining activity.

LOGISTICS

This full-day excursion uses a circular route mainly on well-defined footpaths. The route begins at Keld (limited parking at NY 893013), with Muker as an ideal venue for lunch (Fig. 3.1). The area is an S.S.S.I. and is located in the Yorkshire Dales National Park.

Maps

O.S. 1:50 000 Sheets 91 Appleby-in-Westmorland and 98 Wensleydale & Upper Wharfedale; O.S. 1:25 000 Outdoor Leisure Sheet 30 Yorkshire Dales, North and Central Areas (shows public footpaths very clearly).

GEOLOGICAL AND GEOMORPHOLOGICAL BACKGROUND

Bedrock in the area is upper Dinantian limestones, sandstones and shales ('Yoredale Series') with lower Namurian sandstones (Millstone Grit) capping the highest interfluves. A sandy **diamicton** with blocks of sandstone and shale (probably **till**, but free of far-travelled

erratics) and blanket peat covers much of the fells. The steeper valley sides are relatively free of superficial deposits, although locally there are patches of till and landslide sediments. Most of the valley bottoms contain thick deposits of glacial and debris flow diamictons, **glacio-fluvial** sand and gravel and coarse-grained river gravels, although in the upper part of Skeb Skeugh fine-grained lake peats, **gyttja** and **marls** fill the valley bottom. In some places the valley bottoms are undergoing active incision and waterfalls reflect the differences in rock hardness.

The large-scale landforms of the area are visually impressive and geomorphologically intriguing. The Swale valley crosses the region from northwest to southeast, but takes a sharp right-angle bend at Hartlakes. However a valley of a similar size to the Swale, but with a tiny stream called Skeb Skeugh, extends south of Keld towards Thwaite, then bends sharply towards the east to rejoin the valley of the Swale just beyond Muker. Between these valleys, Kisdon forms an isolated hill some 200 m above the valley bottoms. The origin of Kisdon hill, the changing direction of the Swale valley and the virtually dry valley of Skeb Skeugh have long been a topic of debate.

Many of the small-scale landforms are classical for their type and provide detailed evidence of the direction of ice movement across the region, the pattern of ice wastage, the response of rivers and oversteepened slopes to changes of climate over the past c. 14 000 years and the effects of human activity on river processes. Glacio-fluvial landforms include a variety of glacial **meltwater channels** southwest of Keld, **kames** and **kettle holes** around Angram and Thwaite and **kame terraces** west of Muker. Evidence for climatically driven changes of river activity include a debris flow fan at Hartlakes, and river terraces along the Swale upstream of West Stonesdale Beck. Landforms produced by slope failure include a deep rotational slip at Hooker Mill, a massive debris slide on the northwest side of Kisdon, a massive debris flow at Usha Gap and a block glide at Birk Hill. In the upper part of Skeb Skeugh fine-grained lake sediments below the valley bottom preserve the record of Devensian Lateglacial and Holocene vegetational change, soil development and slope stability. In addition, river landforms show the effects of rock control, of human activity in determining sediment loads, and intrinsic within-channel processes resulting in the formation of large-scale boulder bedforms. The river terraces upstream of Kisdon Force have an extent and elevation determined by rock hardness. Those around Thwaite show the effects of reduced discharge of the present rivers relative to the

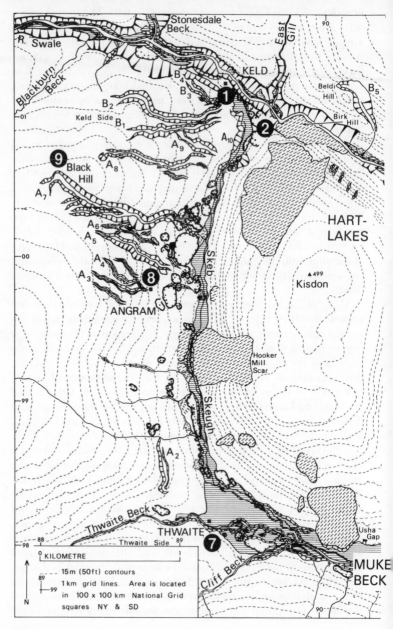

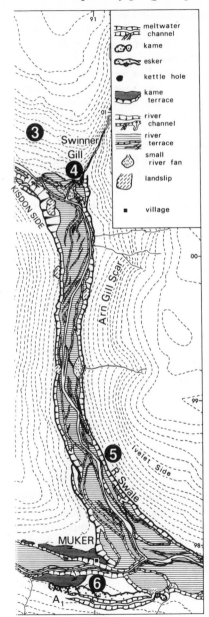

Figure 3.1 Landforms around Kisdon, upper Swaledale, North Yorkshire. Published originally in Rose (1980) and reproduced by permission of Yorkshire Geological Society.

discharges of the rivers that formed the main valley bottom floodplain slopes, while the impressive array of valley bottom terraces south of Hartlakes are the product of within-channel processes enhanced by sediment yield from the local lead mines.

Meltwater channels, **drift** tails, **drumlins** and striations provide the main evidence that glaciation of the region was from the west, and an explanation for the anomalous valley pattern of the Swale and Skeb Skeugh and the origin of Kisdon hill. Meltwater channels indicate that prior to the final melting of this ice sheet, drainage was through Skeb Skeugh and the area between Keld and Hartlakes was an interfluve between the Swale and Swinner Gill. The present valley between these points is ascribed to glacial erosion in response to structural weakness and relatively high glacier energy determined by a steep ice-surface gradient. The kame terraces at Muker indicate a temporary ice-dammed lake between an ice lobe in the Swale valley and a lobe in the Muker Beck valley, and dead ice topography around Angram indicates local ice stagnation. This episode of glaciation was during the Dimlington Stadial (26 000–13 000 ^{14}C yrs BP) of the Late Devensian Glaciation and ice wastage across the region occurred about 14 000 ^{14}C yrs BP.

Pollen from the lake sediments in the upper section of Skeb Skeugh indicates that tundra vegetation colonized the region during the Windermere **Interstadial** (13 000–11 000 ^{14}C yrs BP), but that this vegetation broke down during the severe climate of the Loch Lomond Stadial (11 000–10 000 ^{14}C yrs BP). The mineral content of these lake sediments indicates that accelerated mass movement took place on the slopes during the Loch Lomond Stadial, resulting in the formation of the debris slide on the northwest side of Kisdon. It is probable that the debris flow at Usha Gap and the high fan at the mouth of Swinner Gill also formed at this time.

During the Holocene (10 000 ^{14}C yrs BP to present) vegetation cover returned including extensive woodland, and the rate and magnitude of geomorphological processes was reduced. However, thick glaciogenic sediments and steep valley-side and valley-bottom slopes maintained a paraglacial regime, and relatively high levels of river and slope activity resulted in the formation of important and distinctive landforms. Hooker Mill rotational slip occurred during the early Holocene damming a long narrow lake in the upper part of Skeb Skeugh, and the block glide at Birk Hill continues to move in response to river erosion. River activity has resulted in incision and the formation of river terraces of a variety of origins in different parts of the region, but most significantly, the introduction of mining waste during the 19th century increased the scale and rate of development of these landforms in the section of the Swale downstream of Hartlakes.

For further details see Rose (1980), Rose & Pounder in Boardman (1981, 1985), Rose & Mitchell (1989) and Pounder (1989).

EXCURSION DETAILS

Locality 1. Take the track from the centre of Keld (NY 89300115) to the footbridge across the River Swale (NY 89600105). A poor exposure at NY 89350115 shows rounded boulders in a glaciofluvial ridge formed by meltwater deposition during final stages of ice wastage. The view south across the head of Skeb Skeugh (NY 89400110) indicates a virtually dry valley. A thick sequence of lake sediments underlies this valley bottom. The lake formed in depressions at the base of a subglacial meltwater channel that took the last main drainage down Skeb Skeugh. The view from the footbridge across the Swale shows the gorge which has formed since ice wastage.

Locality 2. Continue along the track and cross the bridge over East Gill as far as the junction with the track to Crackpot Hall (NY 90450085). From the bridge over East Gill (NY 89650115) river terraces can be observed both adjacent to the Swale and to East Gill at levels controlled by hard rock outcrops. Prior to the diversion of the Swale along its present route to the east, East Gill drained southwards and joined the Swale which then flowed down Skeb Skeugh. At NY 90350095 the track crosses the lower end of the Beldi Hill glacial meltwater channel. The sides of this feature are much modified by mining.

Locality 3. Proceed along the track to the footbridge over Swinner Gill (NY 90900050). Below Crackpot Hall (NY 907007) the track crosses an active landslip. Crackpot Hall was built on this landslip and is currently disintegrating in response to this mass movement. In the area around the bridge over Swinner Gill it is possible to examine: (i) the high terrace at the mouth of Swinner Gill; (ii) a river-cut exposure that shows this terrace to be formed of interbedded boulder and cobble beds, sandy diamicton, fine sands, and laminated sands and silts. The slope of the terrace and the **clast** fabric of the sediments show that the feature was formed by Swinner Gill rather than the Swale, and indicate very high sediment loads typical of debris flow processes; (iii) Low terraces formed by Swinner Gill and the Swale in response to high yields of readily available, unconsolidated sediment.

47

Locality 4. Continue along the track to Ramps Holme Bridge across the River Swale (SD 91059860). Well-developed river terraces can be seen adjacent to both the east (SD 91009995–SD 90909965) and west (SD 90650045–SD 90850035) banks of the Swale sloping at an angle steeper than that of the present river. Several poor sections show that these are formed of rounded boulders in a gravel and sand matrix. These terraces formed as fans at the mouth of the Swale gorge but have been dissected as the river eroded upstream as far as Kisdon Force. A small fan is developed at SD 908992 where Arn Gill changes gradient from the steep hillside to the low angle valley bottom. The river between Hartlakes and Ramps Holme Bridge shows well-developed active braiding and adjacent low terraces. These very coarse-grained bedforms have developed here due to the introduction of mining waste into the river. Progressive formation and dissection of these features results in small terraces, which like all the other terraces in the region are of local significance only.

Locality 5. Take the footpath to Muker (SD 91009790). This path crosses well-developed low terraces and river channels that were probably formed as a classical paraglacial response to the transportation of large volumes of sediment during the Lateglacial. Nearer the confluence with Muker Beck the terraces reflect the interaction of the two channels.

Locality 6. Take the footpath to Thwaite (SD 89309820) via a short section of road at Usha Gap (SD 902979). Part of Muker and the eastern section of the path are on a kame terrace (SD 90909790–SD 90509800) which was formed when a lake was dammed between ice lobes in the Swale and Muker Beck valleys. The gradient of this terrace is less than the adjacent rivers reflecting sediment supply from both ice sources. While the kame terrace formed, Kisdon acted as a **nunatak**. West and south of the kame terrace the land is at a lower level, originating as an ice-tongue hollow (around SD 904979). This is now infilled with low-level river terraces formed in response to high flood events, such as that of 1883, when the Swale reached a level of 9.4 m at Keld. At Usha Gap the nose of the massive debris flow extends across the north side of the valley (around SD 901981), having originated from a scar just below Kisdon Farm (around SD 902984). Between Usha Gap and Thwaite the footpath passes a classic nickpoint (SD 89859815) formed at the limit of incision by Skeb Skeugh into the fan of Thwaite Beck. At this point the active floodplain of Skeb Skeugh becomes a fossil terrace. At the south side of

Thwaite Beck small kames can be seen surrounded by river gravels (around SD 896980). These kames must have been formed in the valley bottom during ice stagnation, then, following ice-wastage they have been almost buried by river sedimentation.

Locality 7. Continue along the footpath through Skeb Skeugh to the road at SD 88909940, then along the road to Angram (SD 88759975). Thwaite and the first section of path (around SD 893983) are on the fan of Thwaite Beck. Around Dirty Piece (SD 89159860) the path crosses several small gravel hills and a short north–south trending ridge which are interpreted, respectively, as kames and an **esker** formed beneath the glacier by meltwater draining southward down Skeb Skeugh. The slopes of Kisdon show the effects of mass movement in the form of scree and shallow landslips (around SD 893988), and the massive Hooker Mill rotational slip (around SD 891994). The latter was sufficiently big to block the valley and form a lake. The lake has drained because Skeb Skeugh has now dissected the toe of this landslip (SD 89109950–SD 89059925), but in this section the stream flows in a narrow gorge, in contrast with the open valley to the north and south.

Locality 8. Take the footpath to Black Hill (NY 88150055). This path crosses a series of meltwater channels formed by rivers flowing westward beneath the ice across the Black Hill into Skeb Skeugh. Kames developed in the fields east of the road, just north of Angram (around NY 889000), are composed of sediment transported by these rivers. The meltwater channels dissect one another (i.e. NY 884003), providing evidence for their sequence of development, and indicating that channels become progressively younger towards the north. The subglacial origin of the channels can be demonstrated clearly by number A_7 on Fig. 3.1 (NY 881005), because the topography at the head of this feature does not support a catchment and the channel at Black Hill crosses a watershed with what must initially have been an up-and-down long profile. Such a channel form could only have eroded by confined drainage under hydrostatic pressure.

Locality 9. Walk north along the wall to NY 88200090, then east across the fell to the track (NY 88950090) which joins the road at Keld Youth Hostel (NY 89170097). From here follow the road to the village centre. Gullying is developed at the east side of the wall that runs north across Keld Side in response to improved field drainage. Small exposures show a sandy diamicton with boulders and cobbles of sandstone and shale. Although far-travelled erratics and striated stones have not been observed, this is interpreted as a till deposited by ice that has moved to the region at a relatively high level in the glacier and only intersected the bed in the region of the Swaledale fells. The route eastward across the fell intersects meltwater channel B_1 (Fig. 3.1.), then continues along this channel as far as the road. Channel A_9 can be seen to diverge to the southeast. To the north, Channel B_2 can be seen to run parallel with B_1. Like Channel A_7 these formed without a catchment and are routed across the local watershed. However, these channels drain towards the route of the River Swale from Keld to Hartlakes, indicating that they formed after Skeb Skeugh had been abandoned and meltwater drainage had adopted the course presently used by the Swale. The critical change of direction can be seen at NY 88880088 where Channel A_9 heads southeast, and is dissected by Channel B_1 which heads northwest.

4 · The North Swaledale Mineral Belt around Gunnerside

Dick Ineson *University of Sheffield* and
Brian Young *British Geological Survey,*
Newcastle upon Tyne

PURPOSE

This full-day excursion examines part of the richly mineralized North Swaledale Mineral Belt, hosted by Dinantian and Namurian (Carboniferous) rocks. Spectacular examples of Swaledale's mining landscape will be seen.

LOGISTICS

The excursion proceeds from Surrender Bridge (NY 988999) to the upper part of Gunnerside Gill (NY 940000). For maximum enjoyment it is recommended that arrangements are made for transport to be available in Gunnerside village at the end of the day. Alternatively the route should be retraced from the final locality to Surrender Bridge. The approximate walking distance from Surrender Bridge to Gunnerside is 9 km; from Surrender Bridge to Locality 11 and back, 13 km.

Windproof and waterproof clothing and stout footwear are necessary.

Note: **Do not attempt to enter any of the mine workings** – the tunnels are unstable and the workings are in a very dangerous condition.

Maps

O.S. 1:25 000 Outdoor Leisure Sheet 30 Yorkshire Dales, North and Central areas; O.S. 1:50 000 Sheet 92 Barnard Castle, and 98 Wensleydale & Upper Wharfedale; B.G.S. 1:63 360 Sheet 41 Richmond, and Sheet 50 Hawes.

GEOLOGICAL BACKGROUND

This area north of the River Swale has been called the North Swaledale Mineral Belt. It is the most highly mineralized zone within the broad area known as the southern part of the Northern Pennine Orefield. The ore deposits – mainly in **veins** and **flats** and principally confined to limestone beds – were emplaced in a system of roughly east–west and east-northeast–west-southwest **faults**. The ore mined was **galena**, the major source of lead, although minor amounts of zinc and copper were locally exploited. More recently (in the last 70 years) some of the mines were reopened and **fluorspar** extracted. None are being mined at present, although the occasional reworking of the dumps and tailings heaps has taken place. The dumps are the best source of mineral samples.

EXCURSION DETAILS

Locality 1 (NY 988999). Before beginning the walk up the valley of Old Gang Beck, note the ruins of the Surrender Smelt Mill on the north side of the stream. The ruins of the present mill date from 1839 though two earlier mills, the remains of which are now difficult to discern, occupied the site. Ore for smelting here was brought from numerous mines in the area owned by the A.D. Company. The remains of the peat fuel store can be seen to the east of the mill ruins. The building is unusual in being very symmetrical in plan. The 457 m long horizontal flue – the course of which is clearly visible running northwest from the mill – ended in a small chimney. Smelting here ceased in 1880.

From the north side of Surrender Bridge take the gated cart track which leads west-northwest along the northern side of Hard Level Gill. The lower slopes of the valley are mantled by **till**, though the Main Limestone and overlying **chert** beds may be seen forming scars on the hillside at Barras Top.

Locality 2 (NY 98200014). Under the scar of Smith Hill is the small pile of rubble which is all that remains of High or Raygill Mill. Smelting is known to have been carried out here in the 17th and 18th centuries. Continue up the track for a further 0.8 km to the remains of the Old Gang Mill complex.

Locality 3 (NY 97440052). The Old Gang Smelt Mill, together with its associated buildings and dumps, is one of the most impressive and best-preserved mining sites in Swaledale. The buildings were erected in about 1890. From the furnace house, the horizontal flue was carried over an arch and ran straight up the hillside for 0.8 km to a chimney on Healaugh Crag Edge. The prominent rock outcrops behind the mill are exposures of the Main Limestone, the lowest unit of the local

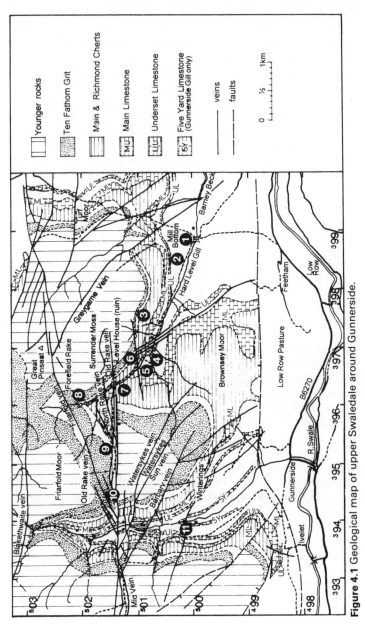

Figure 4.1 Geological map of upper Swaledale around Gunnerside.

53

Namurian sequence. Standing on a bench-like hilltop above the limestone crags about 270 m north-northwest of the smelt mill are the remains of the peat store, one of the most famous relics of the lead industry still to be seen in Swaledale. Lead ore was smelted at Old Gang using both coal and peat as fuel. A year's supply of peat, cut from the surrounding moors during the summer, was stored in the open-sided thatched-roofed peat store, which was some 120 m long and 6.5 m wide. Only the pillars and gables now remain.

Immediately to the west of the peat store the Main Limestone outcrop is cut by a series of prominent gullies which mark the site of opencast trials on minor lead-bearing veins known as the Knott's Veins. No mineralization is exposed here today. The Spence Level was driven from the trackside at the foot of the hillside to explore these veins but little of value was found.

Continue along the track up Hard Level Gill for a further 270 m to the entrance to Hard Level.

Locality 4 (NY 97120068). The partly collapsed entrance to Hard Level lies a few metres south of the track. The relatively modest appearance of this mine entrance belies its importance as the entrance to one of the most extensive sets of underground workings in the Yorkshire Pennines. Driving of the level began in 1785 in the beds beneath the Underset Limestone. The level was driven northwest beneath the valley to reach the group of strong veins, including Old Rake, North Rake and Friarfold Rake, beneath the head of the valley. Considerable lengths of rich lead-bearing vein were worked from this level which was eventually connected with the workings of the Bunton Level in Gunnerside Gill. Adjacent to the entrance of Hard Level, the remains of the old dressing floors and water-wheel pits may be seen. For a time during the 19th century, dressed ore from the Gunnerside Gill workings was transported to the Old Gang Smelt Mill underground via the Bunton and Hard Levels.

Immediately above the **adit** mouth is an excellent exposure of a thin coal seam overlying a **ganister**-like sandstone with abundant rootlet traces.

The extensive workings from Hard Level have produced a very large spoil heap on the south bank of the gill. This is a good locality at which to see a number of minerals. Small amounts of galena, the ore mineral worked, are relatively common, with a little brown **sphalerite** in places. **Baryte** is common in rather coral-like masses of white, chisel-shaped crystals, a form characteristic of this mineral when it has developed by alteration from a barium carbonate mineral such as **witherite**. Pale yellowish-cream witherite may also be found and good examples of white radiating crystalline masses of **strontianite** are occasionally found. Colourless **fluorite** is also present but is rather rare.

The extensive flat, terraced area between the Hard Level entrance and the large dumps is the site of the dressing floors where the lead ore was separated from the waste minerals or **gangue**.

Continue up the track to where a tributuary stream, known as Ashpot Gutter joins the gill from the south.

Locality 5 (NY 96650064). A short detour leads to the large spoil heap adjacent to Ashpot Gutter at the entrance of Victoria Level, a prospecting level begun in 1860 to test the Watersykes Veins. These veins carried **calcite**, baryte and galena which can be found on the dumps. An intergrowth of witherite and strontianite known locally as 'water spar' was also found here, though specimens are very difficult to find today.

Return to the main Hard Level Gill track and continue upstream.

Locality 6 (NY 96780090). Immediately upstream from the junction with Ashpot Gutter, the valley floor contains a flat area of barren silt. This is the settling pond from a small mineral separating plant which until a few years ago was separating barytes (the commercial product consisting of the mineral baryte) from spoil heap material from higher up the valley.

A short distance further up the valley the track bifurcates at Level House Bridge, near which are the ruins of Level House. If time permits it is worth continuing further up the valley to Localities 7 and 8 before returning to this point and following the track westwards over Level House Bridge to Locality 9.

Locality 7 (NY 96400140). Northwest of Level House Bridge the stream is known as Flincher Gill. Between the bridge and Level House it runs on a flat rock bed formed of the Main Chert. Immediately upstream from Level House the valley is crossed by Old Rake Vein, one of the area's main east-northeast–west-southwest trending veins. The course of this is marked particularly in the west by an enormous opencast hush. Hushes are characteristic features of the northern Pennine orefields. They are large opencast workings in part excavated by using torrents of water released from specially constructed reservoirs high on the hillsides. Dumps from levels driven eastwards into Old Rake, and a little further along the track into North Rake,

55

contain a little galena and sphalerite with much baryte. Pale brown 'dry bone' **smithsonite** is present locally. Continue up the track to a ford beyond which there are large dumps derived from the Brandy Bottle Incline.

Locality 8 (NY 96000190). The entrances of the Brandy Bottle inclined adits are now collapsed and difficult to locate. They were driven in the early 1800s to work the Friarfold Vein, a major east-northeast–west-southwest vein, the outcrop of which, a short distance up the valley from these dumps, is marked by an almost continuous line of old spoil heaps and small shafts.

Excellent specimens of several minerals may be collected from the Brandy Bottle dumps. Baryte occurs here in the chisel-shaped crystal form noted earlier, as well as in the characteristic 'cockscomb' variety. Colourless or yellowish-white fluorite may also be found. White radiating crystalline strontianite and yellowish-white compact or radiating crystalline witherite are also present. Some blocks of rather cavernous baryte contain small sprays of colourless **hemimorphite** crystals. Rarer minerals which have also been found here include **cinnabar**, as vivid vermilion-red earthy patches, and beautiful turquoise-blue **aurichalcite**.

Return to Level House Bridge and follow the track westwards.

Locality 9 (NY 95200140). The track follows the extensive spreads of spoil from old workings on Old Rake and North Rake. Specimens of all the minerals so far mentioned may be found in these heaps. In addition, a little bright green **pyromorphite**, a rather uncommon mineral in North Yorkshire, may be found locally.

Continue uphill to where the track begins its descent into Gunnerside Gill.

Locality 10 (NY 94400135). The steep eastern side of Gunnerside Gill is here scarred by several elongated gullies or hushes which mark the course of Friarfold, Old Rake, Watersykes and several other veins in beds from the Ten Fathom Grit at the hilltop down through the Main and Richmond Cherts, and the Main Limestone. Good exposures of all these may be seen in the steep sides of the hushes. Examples of all the area's main minerals are abundant in the spoil from the hushes and from the large dumps from the Bunton and Sir George Levels driven eastwards into this richly mineralized ground. Across the valley the veins may be followed in the conspicuous hushes which mark their course at the Lownathwaite Mines.

If time permits, the walk may be continued by following the hushes down into Gunnerside Gill and following the path downstream to Gunnerside village via the Sir Francis Level mine.

Locality 11 (NY 93990001). The Sir Francis Level was driven northwards, beginning in the sandstone beneath the Five Yard Limestone, to intersect the Friarfold vein system at depth. Driving was begun in 1864 and the Friarfold Vein was cut in 1877. From this level a shaft 79 m deep was sunk to test the veins in the lower beds. Pumping and hoisting were carried out by a hydraulic engine installed in the level. Ore from the Sir Francis Level mine was processed at two dressing plants a little further down the valley. Good specimens of baryte, calcite and sphalerite, accompanied locally by a little strontianite may be found on the dumps. **Barytocalcite** has been recorded here but is very rare.

The footpath can be followed down Gunnerside Gill to Gunnerside village.

5 · The Carboniferous rocks of upper Nidderdale

Albert Wilson *past President,*
Yorkshire Geological Society

PURPOSE

To examine rocks of the Millstone Grit Group (Namurian) and underlying limestones of late Dinantian age.

LOGISTICS

A one-day excursion in two parts requiring transport by car. Part 1 (Locality 1) is at Brimham Rocks, southeast of Pateley Bridge. Part 2 (Localities 2–9) is in Upper Nidderdale, above Lofthouse, beyond which there are no shops or inns. Information about food and toilet facilities is given in the itinerary.

The area around Scar House (Localities 5–9) is owned by Yorkshire Water. A permit must be sought in advance for groups of more than eight people to visit this area from Mr R. Baxter, Yorkshire Water, Western House, Western Way, Halifax Road, Bradford, BD6 2LZ. There is a further restriction on Locality 5: access is only possible from August till February inclusive.

Note: Safety helmets should be worn in the quarry at Locality 5.

Maps

O.S. 1:50 000 Sheet 99 Northallerton & Ripon; B.G.S. 1:50 000 Sheet 51 Masham.

GEOLOGICAL BACKGROUND

Upper Nidderdale lies in the southeastern part of the Askrigg Block, an area of Carboniferous strata gently tilted towards the east. A local **fold** is seen near Limley (Fig. 5.1). The dale is located at the northern end of the main Millstone Grit outcrop of the Central Pennines, which

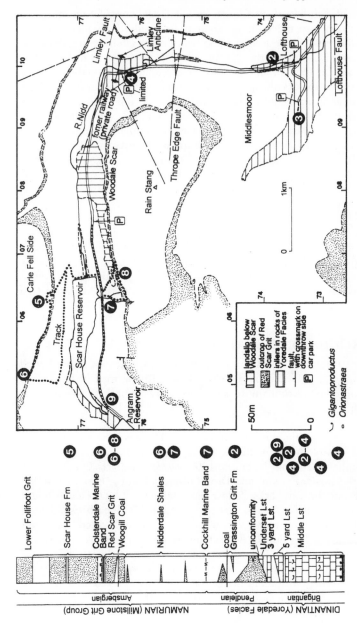

Figure 5.1 Geological map and succession for upper Nidderdale.

extends southwards to Kinderscout. The sequence of sandstones and mudstones are much thinner than in the Bradford–Huddersfield area to the south. There are also fewer bands of mudstone with **goniatites**, the zone fossils of the Namurian. The underlying rocks of late Dinantian (Brigantian) age are of a modified **Yoredale** type and appear in **inliers** along the valley bottom in three separate locations. Individual limestones farther north in Swaledale are separated by thick mudstones and sandstones, but these beds attenuate progressively southwards, so that in Nidderdale limestones are separated only by thin mudstones. A widespread **unconformity** at the base of the Millstone Grit cuts out the highest Yoredale limestones progressively south-southeastwards. Thus at Scar House Dam the surface rests on the Underset Limestone, whilst farther south at Lofthouse it lies on the underlying Three Yard Limestone.

Quarries in upper Nidderdale have furnished much of the stone for the three large reservoir dams built to supply Bradford and now managed by Yorkshire Water. The specific weathering characteristics of the gritstone are well seen at Brimham Rocks, and of the Middle Limestone in the gorge of How Stean. There is a good opportunity to view the deltaic and pro-delta sedimentation of the Millstone Grit sandstones.

EXCURSION DETAILS

Start the excursion at Brimham Rocks. Approach via a southward turning on the B6265 Pateley Bridge–Ripon road (SE 212670) signposted to Brimham Rocks, where a pay car park is located on the right.

Locality 1, Brimham Rocks (SE 208646). The spectacular natural cliffs and tors of Brimham Rocks are carved out of a plateau of Lower Brimham Grit (mid-Namurian). *Do not hammer the rocks*. On a clear day York Minster (41 km) and Drax Power Station (57 km) are visible.

From the car parks, follow paths along the west-facing craggy escarpment in coarse and very coarse-grained **feldspathic** sandstone. The cliffs show many c.1 m units of **cross-bedded** sandstone deposited in fast-flowing delta channels of a river system originating in northern Scotland and Norway. Fretted shapes due to differential cementation can be seen, as well as scattered **quartz** pebbles. At the visitor centre, Brimham Lodge, built in 1792 as a shooting lodge for Lord Grantley, a video presentation on the rocks can be viewed. Refreshments and toilets are available nearby.

Follow the footpath on the north side of Brimham Lodge towards the east. Some of the more bizarre rock shapes are seen here in the 19 m thick grit. The Idol is an *in situ* part of the bedrock with a massive top and a tiny plinth. The greatly undercut base may owe its formation partly to wind erosion after the Devensian glaciation. The Druid's Writing Desk is a mushroom-shaped stone on the escarpment edge. The many tors, like the Dancing Bear, were probably shaped in part by freeze-thaw acting on joints in the grit just after the Devensian glaciation. Return to the car parks past Middle Crags, where further tors with fretted bedding can be seen.

Return via the B6265 to Pateley Bridge, where the Nidderdale Museum may be visited (see p. 203). Drive northwards from Pateley Bridge to Lofthouse, turning right into the village (public car park on the right).

Locality 2, Lofthouse (SE 10057358). Immediately uphill take a path from the left side of the road to a footbridge over the River Nidd. Exposures in Middle Limestone form the foundations of the bridge. Proceed up the west bank for 60 m to view a cliff in the uppermost 4 m of the Middle Limestone, overlain by 1.35 m of mudstone, containing a rib of limestone near the top. The mudstone contains small **brachiopods, bryozoa** and **crinoid** columnals. Some 140 m upstream from the footbridge the mudstone is 1 m thick, still with a limestone layer. At both points the Five Yard Limestone is exposed above, with **cherty** beds in the upper portion. Proceed a further 60 m to a waterfall in Five Yard Limestone and exit to the private road. Walk up the road until a coppice flanks the road on the right. Enter the field by a gate 60 m before the wood and descend to the River Nidd. The Three Yard Limestone with grains of green **glauconite** can be seen in the river bed, but the underlying mudstones are not well exposed. Within the wood are exposures of the lowest beds of the Grassington Grit, a coarse-grained cross-bedded sandstone. Southwards from here, the Grassington Grits are well developed, but they pass into mudstones with thin sandstone to the north, along the flanks of nearby Coverdale. Return along the private road and cross the footbridge into Lofthouse.

Locality 3, How Stean Gorge (SE 094735). Turn right towards Middlesmoor at the junction at the foot of Lofthouse village. A left turn to How Stean Gorge and caves is signposted. There is an admission charge. The feature of interest is a deep gorge with safe walkways for viewing the deeply fretted cliffs in the upper beds of the

Figure 5.2 The Middle Limestone in How Stean gorge, deeply fretted by water erosion (Locality 3). *Photo*: B.G.S.

Middle Limestone (Fig. 5.2). An underground stream can be seen on the south bank emerging from the cave known as How Stean Tunnel. On the north bank is the entrance to Tom Taylor's cave, through which it is possible to walk 180 m and emerge near the car park. However the cave is not lit and torches are needed. Further extensive caves, suitable only for expert exploration, are shown on the plan which can be purchased at the cafe (toilets available).

Locality 4. Rejoin the road and turn right briefly, before turning left up the private road to Upper Nidderdale (parking tickets available at the machine). En route, look right to view the landslip of Thrope Edge, with a steep back scar. Continue northwards past a limestone cliff to the portal of an old railway tunnel, where there is parking (SE 09927647). Descend directly eastwards through the stiles to the River Nidd where the base of the Middle Limestone, resting on mudstone, is seen on the river bed (SE 09947639) close to the axis of the Limley **Anticline**. The delicate tracery of the compound **coral** *Orionastraea garwoodi* var *pristina* can be observed 1.5 m above the base of the Middle Limestone. About 100 m upstream the River Nidd sinks into Manchester Holes, a depression in the river bed; close by on the east bank a cave entrance is seen in which the roaring waters can be heard.

The waters emerge 3 km downstream, below Lofthouse at Nidd Heads. Extensive underground passages, all in Middle Limestone, and completely water filled near Lofthouse, have been explored.

Return to the tunnel mouth where in cliffs to the south the greater part of the Middle Limestone is seen **dipping** southwards on the southern limb of the Limley Anticline. Just south of the tunnel mouth, 2.4 m of dark grey limestones rich in the large brachiopod *Gigantoproductus* are seen close to the axis of the Limley Anticline. The bulk of the fossils are in the original growth position, with the larger, convex (pedicle) valve facing downwards and the concave (brachial) valve acting as a lid. Some 3 m above the top of the *Gigantoproductus* beds and immediately beside the eastern wall of the tunnel, scattered specimens occur of the 1 cm long egg-shaped **blastoid** *Orbitremites*. Higher strata are continuously exposed almost to the top of the Middle Limestone which is here unusually thick and includes the beds seen in the How Stean gorge. These are grey and light-grey limestones, commonly with crinoid debris. There is a further 1 m thick *Gigantoproductus* bed, a fossil rarely found at so high a level in the Middle Limestone of the Yorkshire Dales. In contrast the lower band is very extensively developed. A picnic spot is available at the south end of the cliff.

Rejoin the cars and drive up the Nidd Valley almost to Scar House Dam. Park in the visitor car park on the south side of the valley (toilets available).

Locality 5, Carle Side Quarries (SE 063776). Walk across the dam to the north side and ascend the old incline to Carle Side Quarries (access restricted to August till February inclusive). The three levels of the quarries were developed in 1920–34 to provide stone for the construction of Scar House Dam, which has a concrete core and masonry face. The dam trench was excavated in the highest Yoredale strata and the Grassington Grit Formation. In their heyday the quarries employed 400 men. Looking southwards, another old quarry visible on Rain Stang was open in 1904–15 to provide stone for the Angram Dam, farther up the valley. Note the great landslip of Woodale Scar beneath this quarry, formed by freeze-thaw at the close of the Devensian glaciation. Also one can see the dramatic right-angled bend of the Nidd 4 km to the east. This may mark the point of capture of the eastward-flowing proto-Nidd by a southward-flowing stream.

The lower sandstones of the Scar House Formation in the quarries at Carle Side were deposited by voluminous density currents beyond the mouth bar of a river. These are followed on the second level of the quarry by prodelta sand lobes with **flute marks** on some bedding planes, shown well in fallen blocks from above a bush high on the face. Ascend the dumps to the highest quarry level where medium-grained channel sandstones are displayed. At the undulating base of the higher channel a **conglomerate** with abundant siltstone rip-up **clasts** is well seen. Higher strata are thinly bedded mouth bar sandstones, overlain by mudstones. The skyline feature is in Lower Follifoot Grit.

Traverse the hillside westwards from the highest quarry levels along the top of the feature in the Red Scar Grit. Blocks from the upper half of this grit include abundant crinoid columnals and rarely the brachiopod *Spirifer*. Walk to the second stream, Stand Syke, which drains to an angular embayment in Scar House Reservoir.

Locality 6, Stand Syke (SE 05097784). Here, traces of the Woogill Coal, named after the next major stream east of Carle Side quarries, can be seen in the grit. It has been extensively worked by **adits** and some shafts in Colsterdale to the north, ever since the days of Fountains Abbey. Much of the Colsterdale Marine Beds, some 3 m in thickness, are seen, and the Colsterdale Limestone 2 m above the Red Scar Grit is very fossiliferous. The limestone has weathered to an ochreous orange-coloured 'gingerbread' and contains the zonal goniatite *Cravenoceratoides nitidus*, besides *Anthracoceras paucilobum, Dimorphoceras* and fish remains. Shaly mudstones above the 0.30 m thick limestone have yielded *Eumorphoceras bisulcatum*. The 2 m thick mudstones beneath the limestone yield a **bivalve** fauna. Descend the hill using the gates (do *not* climb the wall) along the rim of Stand Syke, passing cliffs in the Nidderdale Shales which underlie the Red Scar Grit. These beds contain rare thin sandstones and are generally lacking in marine fossils. Join the track and walk east to Scar House Dam. Cross the dam and follow the track on the south side of the reservoir for 350 m.

Locality 7. The stream 50 m east of Scar House Gill (SE 06387654) exposes the Cockhill Marine Band, 1.65 m of very dark mudstone containing bivalves, notably *Caneyella membranacea* and *Posidonia vetusta*, at the base of the Nidderdale Shales. The zone goniatite *Cravenoceras cowlingense* occurs sparsely in the mudstone, and as three-dimensional specimens in limestone nodules near the middle of the mudstone. Other forms, reminiscent of a Yoredale-type fauna, occur in the mudstones, notably crinoid columnals and small zaphrentoid corals.

Cross westwards into Scar House Gill, where the marine band is less well exposed but includes the nodular limestone with goniatites. The overlying Nidderdale Shales consist of 72 m of almost continuously exposed mudstones with a few thin bands of fine-grained sandstone. There are no **seatearth** bands and fossils are scattered plant debris. Above, the Red Scar Grit is in two leaves. The lower leaf is a feldspathic sandstone with seatearth bands near the top, overlain by 0.04 m of attenuated Woogill Coal. The mudstones immediately above the coal yield *Lingula*. The upper leaf of the Red Scar Grit is a cross-bedded medium-grained compact sandstone with scattered crinoid columnals weathering out as voids.

Locality 8. Traverse eastwards along the lip of Nidderdale for 600 m with a fine view across the valley to Carle Side quarries. On the horizon to the north are two **outliers** in Libishaw Sandstone (mid-Namurian), Great Haw and South Haw. En route, cambering effects can be seen on the valley edge, where clefts have opened up behind tilting bodies of sandstone (SE 06807737). Where the track to Middlesmoor intersects the traverse, the two leaves of the Red Scar Grit are well exposed and split by the 0.90 m thick Woogill Coal, worked here by adit. Just east of the track, the upper leaf of the grit is nearly 9 m thick, double the thickness in Scar House Gill and characterized by cross-bedding sets 9 m high and channels within the rock unit. Return downhill to the Scar House car park, using the track.

Look upwards to the scar in the lower leaf of the Red Scar Grit, which contains undulating channel systems. Above the cliff are vast boulders from the upper leaf which have detached due to the cambering effects observed earlier.

Locality 9 (SE 046766). Walk along the road towards Angram Reservoir (cars are not permitted along this stretch) and descend to the south bank of Scar House Reservoir, 300 m down-valley from the Angram Dam. Care is needed, because the exposure is close to the bank of Scar House Reservoir. The sequence consists of 3 m of fossiliferous shaly mudstones with **siderite** nodules, overlain by 5.4 m of unfossiliferous shaly mudstones, capped by 3.6 m of Three Yard Limestone. This is the type locality of the **trilobite** *Weberides barkei*, usually found as headshields, tails or body segments, rather than complete specimens. Also present are zaphrentid corals, bryozoa and a variety of brachiopods and bivalves.

Return to the car park, with views along the road of Scar House Dam, the great landslips below Woodale Scar and finally the major bend in the River Nidd 4 km downstream.

6 · Dinantian and Namurian rocks of Bolton Abbey and Trollers Gill

W. John Varker *University of Leeds*

PURPOSE

This excursion displays Dinantian and early Namurian sedimentary rocks from the northeastern part of the Craven Basin. It begins on the southern flank of the Skipton **Anticline** and passes northwards through the Barden **Syncline** and Skyreholme Anticline before ending at the North Craven **Fault**. There is abundant evidence of mineralization in Trollers Gill.

LOGISTICS

Conveniently split into two half days, each of which may be covered separately. For the Bolton Abbey section, begin at the Abbey car park (SE 071538), and have transport waiting at the Strid car park (SE 058563); walking distance about 4 km. The terrain is easy for much of the distance, but care will be required on the narrow footpath on the wooded east bank of the Wharfe.

The Trollers Gill section begins at the old school house between Appletreewick and Skyreholme (SE 063601) and ends at the top of the mine track at SE 065623, where there is roadside parking. The walking distance for this section is also about 4 km with easy tracks for the whole distance and only one steep section.

There should be *no hammering of any exposures*.

Maps

O.S. 1:25 000 Outdoor Leisure 10, Yorkshire Dales, Southern Area; 1:50 000 Sheets 99 Northallerton & Ripon and 104 Leeds, Bradford & Harrogate; B.G.S. 1:63 360 New Series Sheet 61, Pateley Bridge.

GEOLOGICAL BACKGROUND

The Carboniferous sequence of the Craven Basin is conspicuously thicker than that to the north of the North Craven Fault, and its base is not seen. In contrast to equivalent rocks to the north, these rocks were **folded** and faulted during **Variscan** times into a series of anticlines and synclines which **strike** and **plunge** towards the northeast. Bolton Abbey lies on the southeastern flank of a large, plunging anticline, the Skipton Anticline (Fig.6.1), which is broader and structurally more complex to the west. The first half of the route crosses this anticline and ends on the axis of the adjacent Barden Syncline, covering rocks ranging in age from mid-Dinantian (Skibeden Shale) to early Namurian (Skipton Moor Grit = Grassington Grit). The second half of the excursion crosses the Skyreholme Anticline and is primarily within late Dinantian limestones.

Folding occurred on two scales. The major anticlines and syncline are generally too large to be seen at individual locations, but small-scale **disharmonic** folds, within the Bowland Shales, can be examined in both horizontal and vertical section. Faulting is simple and also strikes to the northeast. Those faults within the limestones of the Skyreholme Anticline tend to be mineralized.

EXCURSION DETAILS

The Bolton Abbey Section

Take the gateway into the Bolton Abbey grounds at the 'hole-in-the-wall' and follow the footpath towards the footbridge.

Locality 1 (SE 075541). Downstream from the footbridge, across the river, is the best exposure of Upper Bowland Shale (early Namurian, Pendleian Stage) in the district. This large cliff, approximately 20 m high, is maintained by erosion at its base by the meandering River Wharfe. Surface weathering obscures details of the structures present but careful observation of the orientation of thin ribs of muddy limestone indicates that several folds are present. Note the bluish-grey colour typical of slightly calcareous shale, and the orange iron oxide (**limonite**) stain which results from modern weathering.

To the right (downstream), the shale is replaced by massive, well-jointed Skipton Moor Grit (Namurian). The contact is clearly a fault, which from this viewpoint appears to be reversed, with the younger grit being thrust beneath the shale. This impression is false;

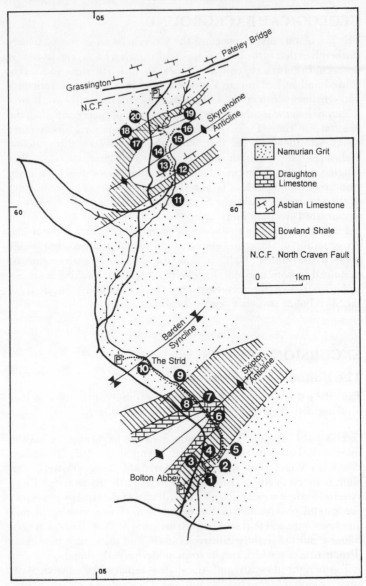

Figure 6.1 (a) Geological map of the area between Bolton Abbey and the North Craven Fault.

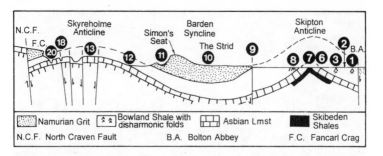

Figure 6.1 (b) Geological section of the area between Bolton Abbey and the North Craven Fault.

viewed from the footbridge along the strike, the fault is seen to be almost vertical.

The erosion of the shale at the foot of the cliff is so rapid, compared with that of the grit, that the river is in the process of cutting its way behind the gritstone, which will be eventually left as a small island.

Locality 2 (SE 076542). Take the footbridge across the river, and look right to confirm the orientation of the fault. About 50 m upstream from the bridge, close to the river, there is a good exposure of well-jointed, friable Middle Bowland Shale (basal Pendleian) which **dips** downstream (southeast) at about 40°. This shale contains a poor fauna of immature fragmentary **goniatites**. Note the excellent **concretion** horizons, formed at an early **diagenetic**, pre-compaction stage.

Locality 3 (SE 075543). Walk 100 m upstream to a point across the river from a small anticline (Fig.6.2). Folds on this scale are common within the Bowland Shale, having been formed during the folding of the main Skipton anticline, when bedding-plane slip concentrated movement within the soft and easily deformed shale, which lies between more competent limestone below and gritstone above. This fold is obvious because of the many thin limey bands. Note that the latter are strongly fractured but remain constant in thickness, whilst the intervening shales have been squeezed into the fold axis. This fold strikes northeastwards across the river and flood plain, cropping out for a second time on the opposite side of the meander.

Locality 4 (SE 076544). Cross the meander along the strike of the fold to the river once again. Here the alternating shales and thin limestones of

69

Figure 6.2 Disharmonic folding in Middle Bowland Shale at Bolton Abbey. *Photo:* J. Varker.

the Middle Bowland Shale crop out along the near-side of the river. Note that the fold is here observed in horizontal section. Most of the outcrop consists of southeasterly dipping beds, but the angle of dip increases downstream to a point where almost vertical shales are seen to be dipping to the northwest. The vertical shale marks the position of the fold axis. Once again, poorly preserved goniatite fragments may be found. The general absence of **benthonic** remains, combined with this distinctive **lithology**, are indicative of anoxic conditions on the sea bed at the time of accumulation.

The view up the Wharfe valley affords an excellent demonstration of river terraces, the most important of which occur at approximately 1.0, 2.5 and 5.0 m above river level.

Locality 5 (SE 078455). Walk upstream for 300 m to a point where the path descends once again to river level. Middle Bowland Shale can be seen cropping out on the opposite side of the river, below the terraces, whilst on the left bank there is a high gritstone cliff. This cliff represents a fault plane, with a spring-line at its base where permeable grit is **thrown** against impermeable shale. Here the downthrow side of the fault is the side with the high relief. This is most likely part of the same fault system which was observed at Locality 1, where the downthrow was in the opposite direction.

Locality 6 (SE 078554). Follow the path upstream through woodland for 700 m to the Storiths road and the ford across Pickles Beck. Cross the ford and continue along the road to a point 40 m beyond the crossroads at the river bridge. Here there is an old, overgrown quarry set in lateral **moraine** left by the Wharfedale glacier. This material is typical of glacially derived deposits in being unsorted and unbedded and includes only locally derived Carboniferous **clasts**.

Locality 7 (SE 076553). Return to and cross the river bridge before turning right (upstream) and entering Strid Woods. (There may be a small charge for entrance.) About 100 m into Strid Woods take a small path down towards the river on the right to Sulphur Well. This well is situated approximately on the axis of the Skipton Anticline where sulphate-bearing groundwater (from **pyrite** in the shale) reaches the surface, the hydrogen sulphide being produced by the activity of sulphate-reducing bacteria. The white filamentous strands in the water of the spring are probably the bacterial colonies. The thick Skibeden Shale from which the water is emanating is very poorly exposed in this region and can only be seen in small exposures along the riverside between this locality and the next.

Locality 8 (SE 075555). Walk 150 m upstream, passing, on the opposite side of the river, well-exposed Draughton Limestone (Late Dinantian, Asbian Stage), to where thinly bedded limestones and shales of the Middle Bowland Shale are folded into plunging anticlines and synclines. One syncline in particular produces the characteristic V-shaped outcrop pattern in the river-bed, the V being directed towards the observer, in the opposite direction to that of the northeasterly plunge. Dips on the limbs of this syncline vary from 60° to 70°. When the water level is high these folds may not be visible.

Locality 9 (SE 073558). Return to the main path and continue upstream for 350 m to an outcrop of gritstone. This marks the position of a small fault striking northeast–southwest, which downthrows gritstone to the northwest. From this point to the Strid the route is over gritstone, the change from variably resistant Bowland Shale to uniformly resistant gritstone being recorded by a marked change in the characteristics of the river.

Locality 10, The Strid (SE 064565). Follow the path upstream to the Strid, a distance of approximately 1 km. At this famous locality, except in times of extreme flood, the entire River Wharfe descends through a series of large pot-holes which originally developed along a joint in the river bed and which have now merged to form a narrow, deep (c. 10 m) channel through which the river flows. Evidence of pot-holing abounds, including some large dry pot-holes on the abandoned margins of the river.

This is also an excellent locality at which to study the composition and sedimentary structure of the grit, but there should most definitely be *no hammering*.

Follow the track up to the Strid car park, a distance of about 1 km, and then drive to the old school-house at Skyreholme. Note that the shortest route, via Barden bridge, is not suitable for large vehicles. The alternative route, via Burnsall, also includes a very narrow road between Burnsall and Appletreewick.

The Trollers Gill Section

Parking is not available at the start of this section so vehicles should be left at the end of the route (SE 065623). From Appletreewick take the road to Skyreholme and Parcevall Hall.

Locality 11, Skyreholme Valley (SE 065602). From this viewpoint there is abundant evidence of glacial deposition by a branch of the main Wharfe glacier. Downstream, the valley is blocked by moraine at its junction with Wharfedale. Look upstream to see the valley partially filled with **drift**, the depth of filling being indicated by the change in slope, vegetation and land use on the valley side to the right. Geophysical evidence suggests that the modern stream (Fir Beck) is not directly above its pre-glacial position.

Walk up the valley and turn left at the T-junction (signed to Parcevall Hall). Immediately before the road crosses Skyreholme Beck take the footpath on the left signed to Gill Heads and New Road. Follow the track as far as the old Skyreholme dam.

Locality 12, Trollers Gill or Ghyll (SE 067614). From Skyreholme Dam, the late Dinantian (Asbian) limestones can be seen dipping downstream (southeast), beneath the topography which consists of Bowland Shale in the foreground and Namurian gritstone in the distance (Simon's Seat).

The view upstream demonstrates clearly the curved southeastern limb of the Skyreholme anticline in the limestone outcrops of the valley side. This area has all the features of limestone country. This limestone is the lateral equivalent of the Draughton Limestone of the Skipton Anticline, but here it is much more massive and has more in common with the Great Scar Limestone of the Askrigg Block to the north. The local water-table is represented by the water surface of Skyreholme Beck; upstream the gradient of the valley floor is steeper than that of the water-table and therefore that part of the valley is dry. This was the worst possible position to have built a dam, since the reservoir would have been impounded entirely upon permeable Asbian limestone.

Locality 13 (SE 067615). Take the track upstream for 150 m and examine the view across the valley. Smooth, curved, overhanging outcrops of limestone mark the points where supra or sub-glacial streams impinged on the valley wall when this valley contained ice. The position of normal faults is marked by vertical discontinuities in the outcrop pattern on the valley walls.

Locality 14 (SE 068616). Take the track upstream to just beyond the stile, where a worked mineral **vein** may be examined on the left, about 20 m above the track. This inclined mineralized fault, close to the axis of the Skyreholme Anticline, was like many others in the region worked for **galena**.

Walk down to the valley floor. Here the valley forks; take the right fork (with Skyreholme Beck), and walk upstream as far as the first of two (sometimes three) springs.

Locality 15 (SE 068617). From this point upstream the gradient of the valley is steeper than that of the water-table and the valley remains dry. The gradient of the water-table is shown by the difference in elevation of the adjacent springs. The screes offer an opportunity to examine the limestone, the dip of which is now gently towards the northwest, i.e. in the reverse direction from that at the dam.

Locality 16 (SE 069618). Walk upstream as far as the boundary wall and look into Jackdaw Nick. This upper part of Trollers Gill is clearly a collapsed cavern, which under normal circumstances is dry.

Locality 17 (SE 066619). Return downstream and take the steep slope up into the hanging valley on the right. Walk up to the spoil tip on the

73

left which marks the position of an old level, where working has taken place for galena. This is another mineralized fault and the irregular nature of the vein can be seen in the roof of the level.

Locality 18 (SE 066621). Walk up the valley, cross the stile and then examine the old workings at a disused mine on the left (Gill's Head Mine or Gill Heads Mine). This mine was the largest in the vicinity and was worked sporadically until recently. The width of the fault zone represents a major fracture and the presence of horizontal **slickensides** indicates that the most recent movement has been in a horizontal direction. ***This area is extremely dangerous and the old workings must on no account be entered.*** This major fracture does not appear on the opposite side of the valley, indicating that it must be displaced by a second fault, which runs up the valley floor. The dip of the limestone is to the northwest, i.e. we are here on the northwestern limb of the Skyreholme Anticline.

Locality 19 (SE 068621). Continue up the track until it passes through a small cutting. Here the track follows the line of a small fault through the limestone escarpment, and affords an excellent opportunity to examine two different **facies** of Asbian limestone. On the right (east side) the limestones contain colonial **corals**, whilst on the left (west side) there are abundant productid **brachiopods**.

Locality 20, Hell Hole (SE 066622). This large swallow hole is just one of a series which mark the junction between the top of the limestone and the base of the overlying Bowland Shale. Since the Bowland Shale is impermeable, run-off is concentrated at this boundary. The important marker horizon, the *Girvanella* Band, may be examined on the flat limestone slabs in the entrance to the hole. This **algal** band marks the junction between the Asbian and the overlying Brigantian and is very widespread throughout northern England.

Return to the track and walk to the parking place. Note the feature of Fancarl Crag to the northwest, formed of Grassington Grit which lies upon the Bowland Shale. The scale of the Skyreholme Anticline can be judged by now looking towards Simon's Seat to the southeast. Fancarl Crag and Simon's Seat both consist of Namurian grit (although not at precisely the same horizon), on opposite sides of the Skyreholme Anticline. The limestone of Trollers Gill is at the anticline's core. The parking place is on Bowland Shale, which is clearly considerably thinner here than in the Skipton Anticline. This shale also contains two prominent limestone bands, each of which produces a marked change in gradient on the road.

Finally, while driving the short distance northwards to the Grassington/Pateley Bridge road, note that beyond the gritstone of Fancarl Crag there are once again the distinctive features of a limestone landscape. This sudden change from grit to limestone marks the southern boundary of the Askrigg Block, at the position of the North Craven Fault, which here has a throw to the south of several hundred metres and runs approximately along the line of the Pateley Bridge/Grassington road.

7 · The Millstone Grit of Almscliff Crag and Harlow Car, near Harrogate

Ian Chisholm *British Geological Survey, Keyworth, Nottingham*

PURPOSE

At Almscliff Crag a typical Millstone Grit (Carboniferous, Namurian) is well exposed, and shows the effect of a gravitational slump that developed during deposition. At Harlow Car, finer-grained sediments can be examined in sequence below the Almscliff Grit. The two localities lie on opposite sides of the Harrogate **Anticline**.

LOGISTICS

This one-day excursion can be split into two half days if required. Almscliff Crag (Localities 1–7) involves scrambling over rocks, and walking boots are needed. The geological meaning of the scenery is best appreciated in low winter sunlight.

Harlow Car (Localities 8–10) includes a stream section and needs wellington boots. This section is best on a bright day in February or March; the summer months are unsuitable because the trees cut out the light, and in autumn the stream may be too full. Access to both is by car, but parking space is limited and neither is suitable for large parties. The walking distance in each case is about 2 km.

Note: Almscliff Crag is on private land, though public footpaths lead to it. The landowner has made it clear that *large parties are not welcome*. The rocks should not be hammered.

Maps

O.S. 1:50 000 Sheet 104, Leeds, Bradford & Harrogate; B.G.S. 1:50 000 Sheet 62 Harrogate, Solid or Drift edition; 1:50 000 Sheet 70 Leeds, Solid or Drift edition.

B.G.S. Memoir, Harrogate (Cooper & Burgess, in press).

GEOLOGICAL BACKGROUND

In early Carboniferous times the area was situated in a subsiding trough known as the Craven Basin, with an area of slower subsidence, the Askrigg Block, not far away to the north. The distinction between block and basin was maintained by periodic movements on the Craven **Fault**-Belt. The top part of a thick sequence of marine mudstones and **turbiditic** sandstones laid down in the basin is exposed in the core of the Harrogate Anticline.

Sedimentation continued into late Carboniferous times without a break, but the area of marine deposition was soon invaded from the northeast by a large river carrying coarse-grained sand, and the sequence rapidly became dominated by its deposits, the Millstone Grits. The section at Harlow Car exposes interbedded siltstones and sandstones, including some **turbidites**, which are thought to have accumulated rapidly on a delta slope in front of the river mouth. The overlying Almscliff Grit is coarser-grained, and is believed to represent the deposits of the river channel itself. The advance of the river may have been accelerated by a drop in sea level.

The advance of the river was brought to an end by a rise in sea level, which caused the delta to retreat for an unknown distance back towards the source area. A thin bed of fossils, deposited in the shallow sea that occupied the area as the sea level rose, has been seen in a temporary section near Harlow Car, but is no longer visible. The fossils collected identify it as the Cravenoceras cowlingense Marine Band, and serve to correlate the Almscliff Grit with the Grassington Grit of areas farther west.

The Almscliff Grit is visible in the Harlow Car area but is more easily examined at its type locality, Almscliff Crag. Here it is possible to work out the flow direction of the river, and to see how the overall shape of the river deposit has been affected locally by a gravity-induced slump, or growth fault (Chisholm, 1981). Repeated advances and retreats of the Millstone Grit river produced a sequence of alternating sandstones ('grits') and mudstones overlying the Almscliff Grit, and some of these beds can be identified in the features of the surrounding scenery.

The deposits of **till** that were spread across the landscape by the Quaternary ice sheets tend to obscure the detail of topographical features related to bedrock outcrops, but the broader outlines are not affected: the harder gritstone beds normally form upstanding ridges and the interbedded mudstones form lower ground.

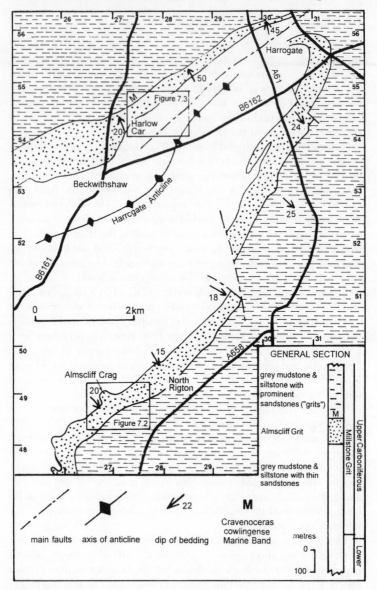

Figure 7.1 Outline geology of the Harrogate Anticline, and main road network.

EXCURSION DETAILS

Almscliff Crag

From the A658 Harrogate–Otley road, take the signposted road uphill to North Rigton. At the west end of the village, turn into Crag Lane and continue past Almscliff Crag to Locality 1. Park by the road (SE 265491).

Locality 1 (SE 265491) is at the roadside. Seen from here, the Crag is clearly made up of two cliffs, each about 15 m high, separated by a flattish slack. Big blocks have fallen off the cliffs. Walk up the footpath to the lower crag.

Locality 2 is the lower crag. Climb up and proceed anticlockwise round the top of it. The Almscliff Grit is a coarse to very coarse-grained sandstone with scattered pebbles of **quartz**. The major bedding planes **dip** northeast at about 22°. Approximately 1 m wide trough **cross-bedding** sets clearly indicate sand transport by currents flowing from the northeast. The cross-bedding can be seen below overhangs and on the top (dip slope) surface of the lower crag.

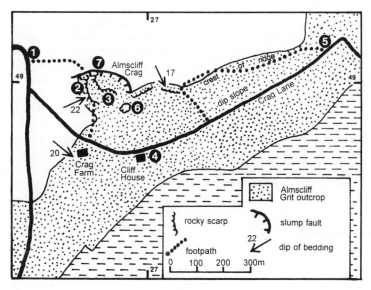

Figure 7.2 Map of Almscliff Crag, showing access to Localities 1–7.

Locality 3 is just across the flattish slack area at the foot of the upper crag. The bedding on this face looks flat, but continue anticlockwise round the base of the cliff until the relationship between cross-bedding and **tectonic** dip again becomes clear. Both are much the same as in the lower crag. Good cross-bedding troughs, again pointing south-west, can be seen on the dip slope of this crag also.

Climb to the top of the crag and look at the view. To the south, a prominent escarpment forms the south side of Wharfedale, from Rombalds Moor behind Ilkley, in the west, through Otley Chevin and Arthington Bank to beyond Harewood, in the east. The escarpment is made up of a series of interbedded sandstones and mudstones in the upper half of the Millstone Grit sequence. They are dipping south beneath the Yorkshire coalfield, most of which is out of sight behind the escarpment. However the television mast at Emley Moor, visible in the distance through a low place in the escarpment above Arthington Viaduct, stands on a sandstone in the Lower Coal Measures. In the far distance, behind the Emley mast and to the right of it, the Millstone Grit appears again, forming the skyline. This is the central Pennine moorland between Huddersfield and Manchester.

In the middle distance, a broad vale occupied partly by the River Wharfe is underlain by softer mudstones and siltstones dipping gently southwards beneath the beds in the main escarpment. Lenticular sandstones form low ridges at Dunkeswick and Huby. Round to the west, the north side of Wharfedale is underlain by a series of gentle southerly-shelving dip slopes in the lowest of the Millstone Grits. These beds crop out also in the rising ground to the north. An intervening slack is underlain by softer beds (these can be seen later at Harlow Car).

Near at hand, to the east and south, the Almscliff Grit forms a continuous grassy ridge with a well-marked 7–10° dip slope slanting down under the mudstones of the middle distance. This dip slope is the one that runs down from the crag to Cliff House; North Rigton is also built on it. The crag is clearly an anomalous feature, a local rocky projection from what elsewhere is a smooth grassy ridge. It is also clear that there is a 90° difference in dip direction between the sandstones in the crag (dip to northeast) and the main dip slope (dip to southeast). The disparity is attributed to syndepositional slump-faulting, caused by instability in the underlying pile of rapidly deposited sediment. The mass of slumped sandstone (the crag itself) is dipping back towards the slump scar, and the fault runs round the north and northeast sides of the crag. The geometry of the feature is the same as that in a rotational landslip. The Almscliff slump moved while sand was being transported across the area, so although the landslip topography was evened out, more sediment was preserved in the slump scar than elsewhere. The general southeastward dip was imposed much later, at the end of Carboniferous times, when **Variscan** earth movements caused widespread folding.

Walk down the path to the road at Crag Farm and turn left.

Locality 4 is on the road by Cliff House. Look up the dip slope towards the crag. The difference in dip direction, and the fact that the crag sandstone underlies the sandstone of the dip slope, can both be appreciated from here. Proceed along the road as far as the first houses in North Rigton and take the footpath on the left, leading back towards Almscliff Crag.

Locality 5 (SE 276491) is at the start of the footpath. At first this runs along the top of the dip slope but eventually it slants across the crest on to the scarp side. Like many of the features formed by sandstones in this area, the ridge is low and rounded, with no clear indication of where the base of the sandstone might lie. This is due to glacial action, which has smoothed off the finer topographical details and smeared a layer of till over all but the highest parts of the ridges. The position of the base of the grit on the map is therefore approximate.

About 200 m short of the crag, the ridge sticks up out of the till, and small quarries reveal sandstone dipping at 15–20° southeast. It is clear that the angle of the dip slope is somewhat less than the dip of the strata. Bevelled dip slopes of this sort are very common in Millstone Grit scenery. Proceed along the ridge to where it joins the crag.

Locality 6 is a small quarry with a pond in it. Poorly bedded sandstone dips to the southeast, whilst immediately to the north, the north-easterly dipping sandstones of the crag appear. There is no obvious dividing line between the two sets of strata, suggesting that the slumped sandstone was still soft when the overlying sandstone was laid down on it, so that the two have blurred into each other. Continue anticlockwise round the north side of the crag. A noticeable break of slope at the foot of the crag here marks the likely position of the slump fault.

Locality 7 is at the foot of the overhanging cliff, where a mud-flake **conglomerate** can be seen. Irregularly shaped holes, up to 10 cm across, show where mudstone pebbles have weathered out. The pebbles are scattered through a 1 to 2 m thickness of sandstone.

Return to Locality 1 via the tumbled blocks. Some are upside down, as shown by the geometry of the cross-bedding. The vertical fluting on some of them must have been eroded by the trickling action of rainwater over 10 000 years, the period since the last ice sheets melted.

Harlow Car

From the centre of Harrogate take the B6162 towards Beckwithshaw. On the outskirts of town, follow the signs for Harlow Car Gardens and turn off down Crag Lane. Park opposite the entrance to the Gardens (SE 281542), and walk down Crag Lane. Take the first side road on the left, past the Harrogate Arms. At the gates to Harlow Car Study Centre, follow the marked footpath leading off right, along the bank of Harlow Car Beck. The stream gradually cuts deeper until it forms a small ravine, exposing the beds that lie immediately under the Almscliff Grit. The dip is steep, so that about 270 m of these beds crop out over a distance of 400 m. Exposure is not continuous, and the location of the clearest sections varies from year to year, depending on accidents of stream erosion.

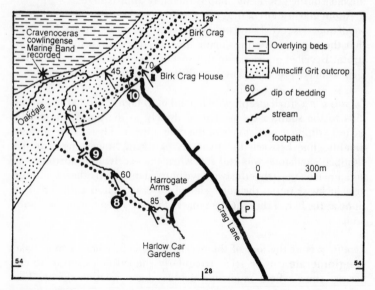

Figure 7.3 Map of Harlow Car, showing access to Localities 8–10.

Locality 8 (SE 27735425) is a chalybeate (iron-rich) spring, covered by a rounded stone canopy. The water emerging is clear, but it gives rise to a rusty deposit as it flows away. This is one of numerous mineral springs that rise in the axial area of the Harrogate Anticline; the Harrogate spa waters are the sulphurous ones. Sandstones and siltstones crop out in the stream bed below, and are exposed at intervals to Locality 9, where access is better.

Locality 9 (SE 27575437) is at a wooden footbridge below a fork in the path. The bridge gives easy access to the stream bed. The base of the Almscliff Grit crosses the stream about 100 m below the bridge, but is not well exposed. The beds below the grit can be seen in the sections on both sides of the bridge. They are dark grey argillaceous siltstones with a great variety of paler-coloured sandstone interbeds, ranging from a few millimetres to over a metre in thickness. Some of the sandstone beds are graded, with **sole structures**, and are probably turbidites. All suggest rapid deposition on a delta slope fed from the mouth of a large river. Instability of these deposits, giving a tendency to collapse under their own weight, is likely to have caused the slump-faulting observed at Almscliff Crag.

Follow the path, which climbs up the east bank of the stream to the lip of Oakdale and along a ridge marking the outcrop of the Almscliff Grit.

Locality 10 (SE 27745463) is just before the path meets Crag Lane, by Birk Crag House, where there are some crags of Almscliff Grit with small quarries. The rock is very coarse-grained (coarser than most of the sandstones in the underlying beds), with small quartz pebbles. The bedding dips steeply (at 45–70°) into the valley, and this side of Oakdale is essentially a bevelled dip slope on the top of the main part of the grit. Trough cross-bedding can be seen on top of some of the steeply dipping beds indicating southwest flow, as at Almscliff Crag. The path continues along strike, past more gritstone outcrops at Birk Crag (SE 27955480), to Cornwall Road, an alternative point of access (SE 28425516).

Walk back to Harlow Car by the direct route, along Crag Lane.

8 · The Carboniferous (Namurian and Westphalian) of the Cliviger Valley, Todmorden

Paul Wignall *University of Leeds* and **Paul Kabrna**
Craven and Pendle Geological Society

PURPOSE

To examine Namurian and Westphalian deltaic **cyclothems**, their sedimentology and fossils.

LOGISTICS

A one-day excursion consisting of the short, but strenuous route of Ratten Clough (2 km), and a longer route taking in Coal and Paul Cloughs (8 km round trip). All routes involve walking over moorland and crossing streams so strong, waterproof footwear should be worn. Cars can be parked in a lay-by off the A646 (T) (SD 889271). Prior permission for access should be sought from Coal Clough Farm, Coal Clough Lane, off Pudsey Road, Cornholme, Todmorden, W. Yorks.

Maps

O.S. 1:25 000 Sheet 690 Rawtenstall & Hebden Bridge; O.S. 1:50 000 Sheet 103 Blackburn & Burnley; BGS 1:50 000 Sheet 76, Rossendale (solid edition).

GEOLOGICAL BACKGROUND

The Cliviger Valley straddles the Yorkshire/Lancashire border and at its head it marks the watershed of the drainage basins of these counties. It is also one of the most spectacular examples of a glacially over-deepened valley in the central Pennines. The incision of a glacial **meltwater channel** down the valley has caused the tributary streams to be left 'hanging' and these are currently actively cutting down into the bedrock, producing the numerous natural exposures of Carboniferous rocks that are the focus of this excursion.

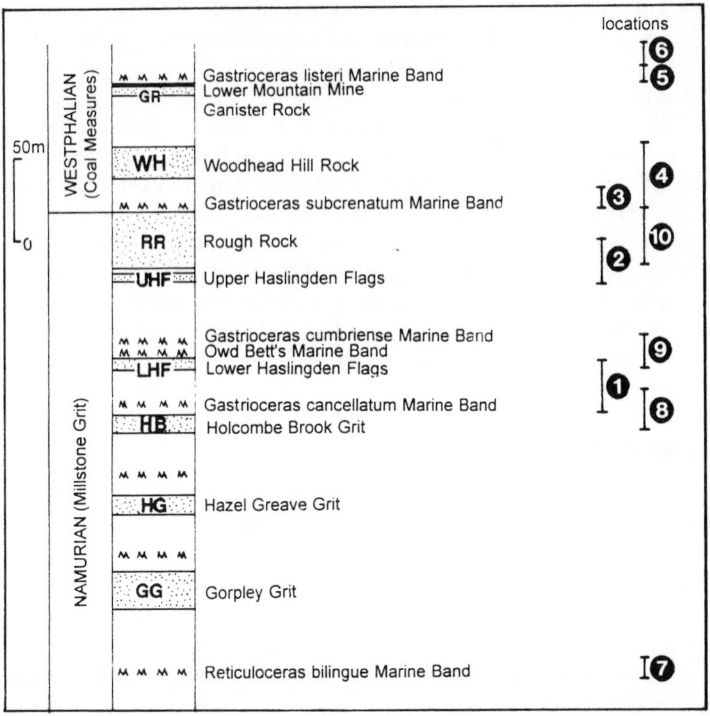

Figure 8.1 Stratigraphy of the Cliviger area showing the sequence exposed at each locality.

The rocks belong to the Namurian Series (usually called the Millstone Grit) and the Westphalian Series (or Coal Measures). Both series are characterized by a repetitive association of rock types caused by the repeated advance of sandy deltas into a deep water basin that occupied this part of the world in the late Carboniferous. These cycles of sedimentation have been called **cyclothems**. They consist ideally of sediments that gradually coarsen upwards from shales through siltstones to sandstones. They are commonly capped by coals in the Coal Measures, though it should be noted that coals also occur in the Millstone Grit, and that their distinction from the Coal Measures is therefore somewhat arbitrary. As will be seen on the excursion, cyclothems are rarely ideally developed and the actual succession commonly consists of shale-siltstone sequences that are sharply overlain by sandstones which can vary greatly in thickness.

The shales at the bases of the cyclothems often contain a marine fauna which includes **bivalves** and **goniatites**. As the goniatites evolved very rapidly, each marine band usually contains a unique and diagnostic species that therefore facilitates their correlation.

There is a fascinating local history of mineral extraction along the line of the Cliviger Valley **Fault**. Evidence for lead mining dates back to the early 17th century when most of the activity was centred around Thievely Farm. Though little evidence remains, there are clues to the mining such as old drifts and spoil heaps (e.g. in the vicinity of Dean Scout, SD 870278), where **galena** and **baryte** can still be collected if you are lucky. Iron also used to be extracted by the early Sheffield ironmasters from the Coal Measures of Riddle Scout where the shales contain common **siderite concretions**.

EXCURSION DETAILS

For those for whom such distinctions are important, the first half of this excursion occurs in Lancashire not Yorkshire.

Locality 1 (SD 891269). The Gastrioceras cancellatum Marine Band is exposed in a small shale cliff and on the water-worn ledges at stream level at this location in the lower reaches of Ratten Clough. The shales of the marine band have been cemented to form a hard, resistant lithology.

A short distance upstream, the Lower Haslingden Flags form a small waterfall. Only 10 m thick here, this sandstone is considerably thicker further to the southwest around Rochdale and Bury where it is quarried for flagstone.

Locality 2 (SD 890267). Ascend the increasingly steep and eventually precipitous Ratten Clough to the base of a superb cliff section of the Rough Rock – the quintessential example of a Millstone Grit, a coarse, **feldspathic** sandstone. In the lower, most accessible part of the cliff, the thin beds of fine sandstone belong to the Upper Haslingden Flags. This again is the rather feeble development of a sandstone which is thicker to the southwest. The Rough Rock, in contrast, occurs throughout the Pennines. At this locality it can be seen to erode down into the Upper Haslingden Flags for 10 cm, but on a larger scale the down-cutting is more spectacular. At Beater Clough, 600 m south of this locality, the erosion has cut down to a level nearly 15 m lower than that seen in Ratten Clough. The basal beds of the Rough Rock contain

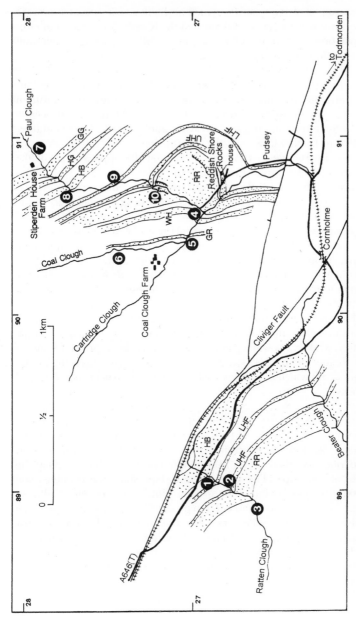

Figure 8.2 Geology around the upper part of the Cliviger Valley, Todmorden.

numerous stems of *Calamites* which probably occurred as log-jams in the fast-flowing rivers that deposited the Rough Rock. The abundant **cross-beds** seen in the cliff face represent cross-sections through sand bars within these river channels.

Locality 3 (SD 888267). Those who have the stamina can make their way around the Rough Rock escarpment to the headwaters of Ratten Clough where the Gastrioceras subcrenatum Marine Band occurs. This contains goniatites and bivalves, and is taken as the boundary between the Namurian and the Westphalian.

It is instructive to view the hillside on the opposite side of the Cliviger Valley from this point. A series of ridges with steep southeasterly and gentle northwesterly slopes represents the expression of several Westphalian cyclothems **dipping** at around 20° to the west – sandstones form the ridge-tops. This is in contrast to the strata just examined on the southwest side of the valley which dip very gently to the southwest. The change in dip and **strike** occurs across the Cliviger Fault which runs along the line of the railway line in this part of the valley. This is a major fault with a **downthrow** of over 200 m to the north, along which patchy deposits of galena have been mined.

For the second half of the excursion, cars are best parked in Cornholme for there is little parking space in the Pudsey Clough valley. Make your way up this valley, noting the impressive crags of the Reddish Shore Rocks at the head of the Clough. This is the Rough Rock again which is here curiously weathered into very large rounded blocks.

Locality 4 (SD 906269). An excellent series of trackside exposures shows the lowest beds of the Coal Measures. The shales above the Rough Rock form a steep bank, although the previously seen Gastrioceras subcrenatum Marine Band is obscured by debris at the base of the slope. The trees on this slope show the characteristic curving trunks produced by gradual downslope movement during their growth – a phenomenon typical of many trees on the steep hillsides of the central Pennines. The Woodhead Hill Rock rests with a sharp contact on the shales and displays well-developed trough cross beds. The shale immediately below the sandstone has been contorted, possibly because of a wholesale downslope movement of the sandstone.

From here proceed northwest up Coal Clough.

Locality 5 (SD 905271). Coal Clough shows a sharp deviation in its course as it cuts down through a thin sandstone, the Ganister Rock. Several interesting features can be demonstrated at this outcrop which help us to understand Coal Measure deposition. The basal contact of the sandstone is erosive, cutting down into the shale (which here contains siderite nodules) for up to 40 cm. Clearly, sand deposition was preceded by an interval of erosion. Within the lower beds of sandstone there are large 'rafts' of coal, a few centimetres thick and up to 3 m wide. The coal does not represent *in situ* growth of plants as there are no roots developed beneath it. However the rafts are too large to have been carried far from their original site of formation. This sandstone probably accumulated in a river channel which was undercutting its peaty banks, causing large pieces to fall into the channel.

Locality 6 (SD 904273). If permission has been obtained at Coal Clough Farm, ascend the upper reaches of Coal Clough to where an impressive 100 m long cliff section displays a variety of Coal Measure shales. At the base of the cliff, the Lower Mountain Mine coal seam is developed with a sandstone rib at its centre. This is directly overlain by the Gastrioceras listeri Marine Band, which contains goniatites and several species of bivalve including the spectacular, radially ribbed *Dunbarella papyracea*. The marine band contains large bullions (carbonate concretions) which formed early in the burial history of the shale, thereby preserving the goniatites in an uncompacted state. Occasionally the chambers of the goniatites contain a viscous, green oil rather like *Swarfega*, presumably the decomposed remains of the goniatite animal itself.

The following sections in Paul Clough can either be examined by returning to Locality 4 or, as described here, by crossing the moorland from Locality 6 to Stiperden House and walking downstream. The dip of the rocks in Paul Clough is rather steep which means that an exceptionally large amount of Namurian stratigraphy can be seen over a relatively short distance.

Locality 7 (SD 910279). In a small shale bank, the goniatite *Reticuloceras bilingue* occurs in rather flaky, grey shales. This is a notably different goniatite-bearing lithology to the fissile black shales of the Gastrioceras listeri Marine Band of the previous locality.

Walking downstream from this locality, two thin sandstones can be seen to cross the valley but the intervening shales are not exposed.

Locality 8 (SD 907276). The third sandstone, the Holcombe Brook Grit, and its overlying shales, is rather better exposed. In many parts of this region this Grit is capped by a good-quality coal, one of the oldest hereabouts. However at this locality a cannel coal is developed, a much poorer quality shaly coal that is formed by the transport and deposition of vegetation in pools and ponds. The cannel coal sits on a **seatearth** containing curious lumpy concretions.

Around 30 m downstream from the top bedding plane of the Holcombe Brook Grit, the Gastrioceras cancellatum Marine Band occurs at stream level. The fossils are rather poorly preserved at this locality.

Locality 9 (SD 907273). Further downstream, the Lower Haslingden Flags intersect the stream. Around 2 m above the top of the sandstone a hard-weathering, fissile, black shale sits on a horizon of contorted shale. The appearance of this shale and its geochemical attributes are identical to that of marine band black shales; this is the newly discovered Owd Bett's Marine Band. It is named after a type locality north of Bury. The only marine fauna consists of rare **conodont**

Figure 8.3 Locality 9: Lower Haslingden Flags at left of outcrop overlain by softer weathering siltstones. The hammer denotes the position of Owd Bett's Marine Band; the Gastrioceras cumbriense Marine Band occurs in soft weathering shales behind the rucksack. *Photo*: P. Wignall.

microfossils. More of these marine bands without goniatites probably await discovery in the Pennines. The Gastrioceras cumbriense Marine Band occurs a further 2 m above the Owd Bett's Marine Band at the top of the section (Fig. 8.3).

Locality 10 (SD 907272). This splendid gorge in the Rough Rock allows nearly the entire 34 m thickness of the sandstone to be examined. In the upper part of the section, cross sets up to 8 m in height can be discerned – testimony to the presence of large dunes or bars that must have formed in a channel of appreciable depth.

9 · The Upper Carboniferous of the Halifax area

Brian Turner *University of Durham*

PURPOSE

The object of this excursion is to examine the sedimentary **facies** and depositional environments of the upper part of the Namurian Millstone Grit and the lower part of the overlying Westphalian A Coal Measures.

LOGISTICS

The excursion can be completed in one short day as all the localities occur within 10 km to the south and southwest of Halifax (Fig. 9.1) and are easily accessible by road. Very little off-road walking is required and the distances involved at individual outcrops are less than 1 km, mostly over footpaths and rough tracks. Care must be excercised when visiting outcrops in quarries and road cuttings, and hard hats are recommended for safety. Private transport is an advantage but not essential, and parking facilities are available at all localities. The excursion is not suitable for large parties.

Prior permission should be sought for access to Clockface Quarry from Marshalls, Brier Lodge, Southowram, Halifax, HX3 9SY (tel. 0422 366666).

Maps

O.S. 1:50 000 Sheets 110 Sheffield & Huddersfield and 104 Leeds, Bradford & Harrogate; B.G.S. 1:50 000 Sheet 77 Huddersfield.

GEOLOGICAL BACKGROUND

Halifax lies within the central Pennines, which form a prominent topographic feature throughout northern England, comprising steep, flat-topped hills and plateaux up to 600 m above sea level, dissected by deep river valleys and cloughs. Most valleys were incised into pre-existing broader, higher-level valley features during late Tertiary times. A good example of this is the River Calder, which flows eastwards through the area (Fig. 9.1) in a steep-sided valley incised between prominent shoulders defining the edges of an older, high valley floor.

Geologically the Pennines consist predominantly of Carboniferous sandstones, shales and limestones folded, during the **Variscan Orogeny**, into an asymmetric **anticline** with the steeper limb in the west. In the central Pennines, late Carboniferous (Namurian and Westphalian) sediments form a low scarp on either side of the north–south trending Pennine anticlinal ridge. Apart from a few exposures along the scarp crest, most outcrops are confined to old quarries.

In early Carboniferous (Dinantian) times the structure of northern England consisted of a number of basins and blocks, initiated in response to reactivation of pre-existing lines of crustal weakness by a south-southeast–north-northwest directed extensional stress field. In the Pennine Basin, continued extension led to its further break-up into a number of small, tilted fault blocks, forming a series of **half-graben** basins. Thus the north Pennine Basin can be divided into the Huddersfield Basin in the east, and the Rossendale Basin in the west, separated by the Rossendale Ridge. Rapid **fault** controlled basin subsidence continued until late Namurian times, followed by a gradual change to a more general phase of thermal subsidence. Thicker, more argillaceous sediments accumulated within the more rapidly subsiding basins with thinner or condensed sequences over the more stable blocks.

In Namurian times the Huddersfield Basin was filled initially with sediment supplied by northerly sourced, **turbidite**-fronted, deep water delta systems. As the basin shallowed the deltas, now lacking turbidites, assumed a sheet-like geometry and the basin gradually evolved into a low relief alluvial plain by the beginning of the Westphalian. Deposition was characterized by a cyclic repetition of strata, each cycle being bounded by laterally persistent marine bands related to **eustatic** sea level changes. In late Namurian times braided rivers flowed to the southwest, past Leeds, and to the south and southeast as far as Sheffield, located at this time on the northern margin of the Gainsborough Trough which was occupied by a standing body of fresh or brackish water characterized by low wave and tide energy.

The upper part of the Namurian Millstone Grit seen on this

93

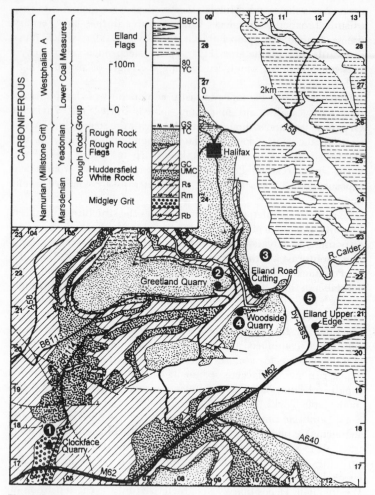

Figure 9.1 Generalised geological map and vertical section of the Halifax area.

Rb = Reticuloceras bilingue Marine Band; Rm = Reticuloceras metabilingue Marine Band; Gc = Gastrioceras cancellatum Marine Band; Gs = Gastrioceras subcrenatum Marine Band; UMC = Upper Meltham Coal; TC = Thin Coal; 80YC = 80 Yard Coal; BBC = Better Bed Coal.

excursion includes the Midgley Grit and the Rough Rock Group which are equivalent in age to the middle part of the Marsdenian and the Yeadonian Stages respectively (Fig. 9.1). In the Halifax area, the Rough Rock Group comprises a braided channel sheet sandbody, known as the Rough Rock, scoured into sandstones and siltstones of the underlying Rough Rock Flags. Halifax is largely built of locally quarried Rough Rock sandstone, and the River Calder on the south side of the town has cut down through these sandstones forming a deep, well-wooded valley in the underlying shales. When traced westwards into the deeper, more rapidly subsiding Rossendale Basin, the Rough Rock is underlain by the Upper and Lower Haslingden Flags, interpreted as the bar finger sands of an easterly **prograding** birdsfoot delta similar to the present-day Mississippi delta. In contrast, the Rough Rock Flags, which are equivalent to the Upper Haslingden Flags, are interpreted as the distal deposits of a lobate, shallow water delta prograding to the southwest.

Coal Measures **conformably** overly the Millstone Grit and show a similar pattern of deposition, except that sandstones are thinner and finer grained, coal seams are thicker and more abundant, non-marine **bivalve** bands are common, and marine bands are rare. The coals are mostly bituminous coals, underlain by **seatearths** comprising soft **fireclay** and hard **ganister**, some of which have been exploited commercially between Halifax and Sheffield for making firebricks and furnaces. The most prominent sandstones in the lower part of the Coal Measures, some 165 m above the base, are the locally named Elland Flags (Fig. 9.1). These are still worked extensively around Halifax for flags and roofing slates.

The description of the outcrop in Greetland Quarry and the Elland Road Cutting is based on the work of Bristow (1993 and earlier work) augmented by the author's own field observations.

EXCURSION DETAILS

Locality 1, Clockface Quarry (SE 046175). The quarry is situated next to the B6114 Rochdale Road between Ringstone Edge Reservoir and the M62 Motorway and illustrates a distributary channel sandbody and interdistributary bay-fill deposits. This is a working quarry and prior permission is required for visits. The quarry provides good, two-dimensional exposures of the Namurian Midgley Grit (Fig. 9.2a), located between the Reticuloceras bilingue Marine Band and the Reticuloceras metabilingue Marine Band in the middle of the Marsdenian (R_2) Stage (Fig. 9.1). The base of the quarry face consists of about 2 m of incompletely exposed, burrowed and **bioturbated**, plant-rich, fine micaceous sandstone and siltstone containing locally rippled sandy intervals. These are sharply overlain by trough **cross-stratified**, coarse to very coarse, granular and pebbly sandstone containing abundant carbonaceous plant material, commonly concentrated on **foresets** and the base of troughs (Fig. 9.3). Softish weathered, brown, iron-rich nodules and lenses occur at intervals in the sandstone. The northern end of the quarry, which has been locally affected by a northwest–southeast trending fault, reveals the presence of large-scale cross-strata **dipping** in opposite directions with individual foresets internally structured by trough cross-stratification, plane lamination and low angle lamination (Fig. 9.2a). These are interpreted as mid-channel or bank-attached sand bars within a major distributary channel, scoured into the abandonment, or bay-fill deposits beneath.

Locality 2, Greetland Quarry (SE 095216). Access to the quarry is by the steps and footpath at the top of the road behind Coronation Street, which can be reached from Clayhouse Lane off the B6113 Ripponden Road. The quarry face provides a rare example of lateral accretion surfaces within the braided river sandbody of the Rough Rock, structures which are more typical of point bars in meandering rather than braided river systems. The 6.5 m high quarry face exposes a series of 30 m long lateral accretion surfaces dipping at <15°, but decreasing in dip and flattening to the west where they appear to be overlain and draped by cross-stratified sandstone deposited by currents flowing to the west. Lateral accretion units defined by these bounding surfaces contain mainly small-scale cross-stratification, trending southwards out of the quarry face at a high angle to the bounding surfaces. Water escape structures and undulatory laminations occur at the westernmost end of the outcrop, above a 2 m thick cross-stratified unit. The sandstone is coarse to very coarse-grained but with no systematic variation in the grain size or scale of the sedimentary structures within individual lateral accretion units, a feature which is atypical of point bars.

At the eastern end of the quarry face, the accretion surfaces steepen and are replaced by large-scale cross-stratification within a coarser-grained, more pebbly sandstone, possibly representing the nucleus around which the sandbody accumulated (Bristow, 1993), probably as a large medial bar within the Rough Rock braided distributary channel system.

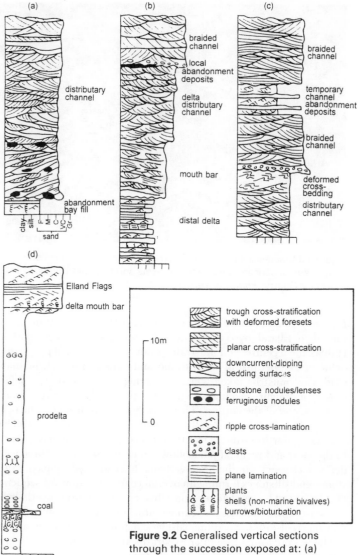

Figure 9.2 Generalised vertical sections through the succession exposed at: (a) Clockface Quarry (SE 046175); (b) Elland Road Cutting (SE 103215); (c) Woodside Quarry (SE 099209); (d) Upper Elland Edge (SE 118204). See Fig 9.1 for locations.

Figure 9.3 Small-scale trough cross-stratification with carbonaceous plant material concentrated on the foresets and base of troughs, Clockface Quarry. *Photo*: B. Turner

Locality 3, Elland Road Cutting (SE 103215). The road cutting lies on the A629 Elland bypass (Calderdale Way), some 4 km south of Halifax town centre, and illustrates a fluvially dominated prograding delta system. Because of heavy traffic, and its location on a bend in the road, care must be taken when examining the outcrop. The safest, most convenient parking is on the extensive grass verge at the southern end of the cutting. The cutting varies in height from 15 to 30 m and can be traced laterally for some 500 m. The outcrop, which is orientated north-northeast–south-southwest, approximately parallel to the local and regional palaeoflow direction, consists of three well-defined channel sandbodies overlying finer-grained rippled sandstones and siltstones forming an overall coarsening-upward sequence (Fig. 9.2b). The sandstones and siltstones are sharply overlain by coarser-grained micaceous sandstones, internally structured by downcurrent-dipping bedding surfaces, defining downstream accreting beds, containing trough cross-stratification and occasional plane lamination. The sandstone and siltstone beds at the base of the outcrop were deposited in the distal part of a delta system with the overlying coarser-grained sands laid down in a more proximal (landward) mouth bar setting as the delta prograded basinwards.

The mouth bar sands are overlain by two coarse to very coarse, mainly trough cross-stratified, erosive, channel sandbodies forming concave lenses up to 7 m thick and 300 m wide, interpreted as delta distributary channel sandbodies deposited by palaeocurrents flowing to the southeast. The top of these amalgamated sandbodies is truncated by the sediments above, or conformably overlain by a locally developed thin lens of fine sandstone and siltstone indicative of channel shifting and abandonment. The upper channel sandbody differs from those below in its multistorey sheet-like geometry and internal scour surfaces, commonly strewn with wood fragments. It is an erosively based, coarse to very coarse, granular, **feldspathic** sandstone, internally dominated by trough and solitary planar cross-stratification, deposited by palaeocurrents flowing south. Deformed foresets occur near the top of the outcrop.

The sandstone is correlated with the Rough Rock, and is thought to have been deposited in a braided river channel characterized by low to moderate discharge fluctuations. The thickness and lateral continuity of the sediments at this locality indicate that the delta supplied by this river system was probably of the shallow water, lobate type.

Locality 4, Woodside Quarry (SE 099209). Easiest access to the quarry is from Woodlands Lane, off the B6112 Holywell Green Road. The Rough Rock exposed in the quarry face consists of braided river sandbodies showing **tectonically** induced deformation features, and occurs at about the same stratigraphic level as the outcrop in Greetland Quarry. Good views of Greetland Quarry and especially the Elland Road cut section can be seen from this locality. The outcrop exposed in the quarry face is up to 13 m high and can be traced laterally for some 150 m. The lower part of the outcrop consists of a coarse-grained, plant-rich channel sandstone with low-angle trough cross-stratification and rare solitary planar sets, deposited by palaeocurrents flowing south-southwest. The top of the sandstone is characterized by a laterally persistent 1.5 m thick zone of deformed cross-stratification (Fig. 9.2c) showing local flexuring of foresets, oversteepened foresets, overturned and recumbently folded foresets, and convolute foresets. The thickness and lateral persistence of this unit suggests that deformation may be related to contemporaneous tectonic activity.

The lower sandstone is overlain by a much coarser-grained, erosively based channel sandbody downcutting to the southwest (Fig. 9.2c). Concentrated along the erosion surface are granules and small pebbles of **quartz**, and shale and siltstone **intraclasts** and lenses, together with abundant plant material including well-preserved *Calamites* stems. Internally the sandstone is structured by trough cross-stratification, except at the southwestern end where it contains a 2 m thick bed of ripple cross-laminated fine sandstone with rare small trough cross-stratification (Fig. 9.2c).

Locality 5, Upper Elland Edge (SE 118204). This outcrop of a prograding shallow water delta system is best accessed by the footpath leading off the B6114 Mirfield Road by the Eurogas Depot. The outcrop is orientated north-northeast–south-southwest and consists of some 15 m of black shale coarsening upwards at the top into a 30 cm thick zone of silty shale and ripple cross-laminated micaceous siltstone and fine sandstone, sharply overlain by the Elland Flags (Fig. 9.2d) which are only accessible at the southernmost end of the outcrop. The black shales are usually finely laminated and contain ironstone nodules and nodular layers that decrease in thickness and abundance upward through the succession, a thin coal seam, and 3 thin non-marine bivalve bands (Fig. 9.2d). The overlying Elland Flags are fine, locally burrowed, micaceous sandstones, containing ripple cross-lamination with some plane lamination, low-angle lamination and cross-stratification deposited by currents flowing to the southwest. The sequence occurs at the base of the *Carbonicola communis* non-marine bivalve **Biozone**, and is interpreted as the prodelta shales and delta front sands (Elland Flags) of a prograding shallow water delta system.

10 · Middle and Upper Carboniferous rocks (Millstone Grit and Coal Measures) of the Sheffield region

Mike Romano and **Martin Whyte**
University of Sheffield

PURPOSE

The first part of this excursion examines the sediments and fossil plants of the Millstone Grit, scarp and dip scenery, industrial archaeology (millstones) and Iron Age fortifications. The second part illustrates Coal Measure sediments, with fossil plants, fish, and non-marine **bivalves**.

LOGISTICS

The two excursions lie within an 11 km radius of Sheffield. In stratigraphic order, Excursion 10a (Burbage Edge; Namurian, Millstone Grit) should be taken first. This starts from Upper Burbage Bridge (SK 261830), which may be reached by car from Sheffield via the A625 and Hathersage, or by Ringinglow Road from the A625 at Ecclesall Church (SK 335833). By bus, take routes 240, 272, or X65 from Sheffield and alight just beyond Fox House Inn (SK 263806); the excursion will then be started at Locality 4. Off-road parking is available for a number of cars or minibuses just to the west of Upper Burbage Bridge; limited road parking also exists to the east of the bridge. Allow a day or long half-day, involving approximately 6 km of footpath walking with occasional scrambling over boulder fields and exposures along streams.

Excursion 10b (Westphalian, Coal Measures) is a disused quarry at Bradgate Brickyard (SK 413935) near Rotherham, northeast of Sheffield, requiring 1–2 hrs. Take the A6109 from Sheffield to approximately 300 m north of the junction with the A629. Parking is limited to minor roads to the west of the quarry and coaches are advised to find parking elsewhere.

Note: Permission must be sought from Mr Watson, Grange Farm, Kimberworth, Rotherham before visiting Bradgate Brickyard. *Hard hats are recommended for these excursions* since some of the localities are below cliffs.

Maps

O.S. 1:50 000 Sheets 110 Sheffield & Huddersfield, and 111 Sheffield & Doncaster; B.G.S. 1:50 000 Sheets 100 Sheffield and 87 Barnsley.

GEOLOGICAL BACKGROUND

The upper part of the Millstone Grit to the southwest of Sheffield is dominated by thick sandstone units interbedded with shales. Occasional marine incursions and subaerial exposure of the delta top gave rise to thin marine bands and the development of coals. One of the sandstones, the Rivelin (or Chatsworth) Grit, forms characteristic scarp features such as Stanage Edge, Burbage Edge and Millstone Edge. The grit is of upper Namurian (Marsdenian) age and consists of an upper and lower leaf. It is bounded below by the Reticuloceras superbilingue Marine Band, and above by the Ringinglow Coal. The grit is a major sandbody which was laid down in a **fluvial** setting as part of the advancing delta system from the north. The sandstones of the Rivelin Grit are coarse grained, occasionally pebbly, and show excellent examples of **cross-bedding** on a variety of scales. Different **facies** are present within the grit, characterized by the presence or absence of pebbles and the scale and type of the cross-bedding. The shales below the lower leaf contain rare **goniatites**. Drifted plant remains are more common in both the sandstones and shales. The rocks generally **dip** very gently to the east, although there are local variations, but the considerable downcutting of Burbage Brook has created an **inlier**, exposing the beds underlying the Rivelin Grit along most of its course.

The Coal Measures overlie the Millstone Grit to the east and, owing to their similar **lithological** characteristics, give rise to comparable (though generally more subdued) topographic features. Bradgate Brickyard (Excursion 10b) is located in urban Rotherham, and the gently dipping sequence of middle Coal Measures provides a convenient way to see a variety of rock types (sandstones, siltstones, shales, thin coals, **seatearths**), sedimentary structures (cross-bedding, slump structures, lamination) and fossils (plant fragments, **bivalves**, **brachiopods** and fish remains) within a typical Coal Measure sequence. The coarsening-up cycles within the Coal

Measures reflect alternating **regressive** and **transgressive** events, and represent a deltaic/fluvial environment in which periods of emergence led to the growth of luxuriant forests.

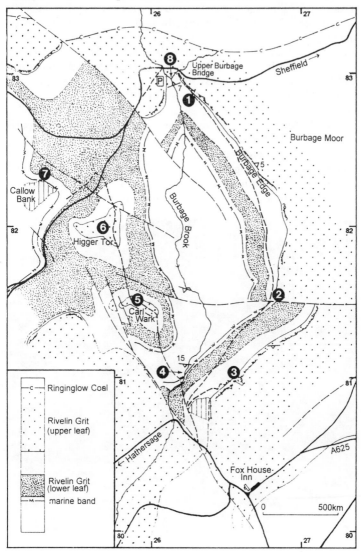

Figure 10.1 Simplified geological map of the Burbage area.

EXCURSION DETAILS

Excursion 10a

From Upper Burbage Bridge (Fig. 10.1), walk to the east and take the signed footpath through the gate in the wall. There is a fine view of the area from here with the main scarp of the upper leaf of the Rivelin Grit extending 2.5 km to the south. Note also the termination of the line of crags (by a **fault**) to the west of Burbage Brook, and the prominent hills of Higger Tor and Carl Wark (see Localities 5 and 6). Follow the footpath south for approximately 100 m.

Locality 1 (SK 262829). Cross-bedded sandstones are well exposed along the scarp edge in this area (Fig. 10.2). The rock is a typical 'grit'; a coarse-grained **feldspathic** sandstone with common pebbly layers. The grains are subangular and consist of colourless **quartz**, pink/cream-coloured weathered feldspars, and occasional **mica** flakes. The rounded pebbles are dominantly of **vein** quartz. Cross-bedding is

Figure 10.2 Large-scale cross-bedding in the upper leaf of the Rivelin Grit (Locality 1). *Photo*: M. Romano.

ubiquitous and **foreset** beds at this locality commonly indicate a transport direction towards the northwest. The rocks are well-jointed along two dominant directions (northwest–southeast and northeast–southwest).

Continue south along the sandy footpath (material derived from adjacent sandstones), noting marshy patches with rushes and mosses near the footpath where water passing through the permeable and porous sandstones meets the impermeable shales underneath (see Locality 4), and seeps out at the surface as springs. Also note the large-scale foreset beds in the scarp and the land surface strewn with boulders resulting from **solifluction**.

Locality 2 (SK 268815). After about 1 km the prominent scarp becomes less well-defined. Just to the south the scarp becomes much more prominent again but is some 400 m to the east of the path. This abrupt change in position is due to a fault **downthrowing** to the north. However, to the west, of the prominent flat-topped hills Carl Wark (see Locality 5) and Higger Tor (see Locality 6), Higger Tor to the right (north) is over 45 m higher, indicating its relative upward displacement. A further 500 m along the footpath to the southwest, a large quarry is visible in the scarp to the east. Leave the path and ascend to this quarry, taking care as you go through the boulder field below the quarry entrance.

Locality 3 (SK 266810). The Rivelin Grit here has been extensively quarried and the 20 m high, vertical joint faces (popular among climbers) show large foreset beds dipping towards the south. Numerous millstones, in various stages of completion, lie around the quarry entrance; some are up to 1.9 m across and nearly 0.4 m thick. Also visible in the adjacent scarp to the south of the quarry are boreholes showing the method of extraction of the sandstone blocks. Follow the quarry path obliquely across the boulder field to the southwest and pass through the old stone gate posts along the track to the quarry approximately 60 m from the junction with the main footpath. There is a fine example of a stone trough (difficult to locate when the bracken is high), and yet more millstones, just before the junction with the main path. Take the minor track (at SK 262808) to the northwest, towards Burbage Brook, where there are small exposures of shales which underlie both leaves of the Rivelin Grit.

Locality 4 (SK 262809). A larger exposure occurs on the west bank 75 m further north (access via the west bank). Here, fissile dark-grey shales dip towards the south-southwest; fossils have not been recorded. Return to where the path crosses the stream and continue along a track in a north-northwest direction.

Locality 5 (SK 260814). At Carl Wark the Rivelin Grit may be examined and palaeocurrent directions determined. A few millstones may be seen among the boulders on the eastern slopes of the hill. Carl Wark (Earl Wark on old maps) is the site of an Iron Age Fortification (2500–2000 years old) and on the western side of the hill a 7 m wide earth rampart and a 2 m high stone wall form impressive reminders of the fort. A former entrance and stone trough (Iron Age or Roman) can also be seen and an information plaque is located near the entrance. The footpath route then continues in a north-northwest direction to Higger Tor.

Locality 6 (SK 806819). From Higger Tor there are splendid views of Burbage Edge, Carl Wark and the form of the Burbage inlier, as well as further scarp edges of the Rivelin Grit at Over Owler Top towards the south-southwest. Note the pebbly nature of the grit and various scales of cross-bedding. The direction of transport may be measured and compared to that at the previous localities.

The quickest way back to the car park and Locality 8 is to drop down to the road on the footpath, over steps recently constructed to combat erosion, and then turn right. However, if time permits, an additional locality may be visited at Callow Bank where the lower leaf of the Rivelin Grit is exposed. From Locality 6, cross the road after having descended from Higger Tor and take the footpath opposite. After about 40 m another path is reached; turn left and continue for some 100 m before branching off to the right and follow the contours to the prominent scarp and landslip area of Callow Bank.

Locality 7 (SK 252823) At Callow Bank 10–15 m of dark grey shales, with occasional flat, tabular **sideritic** nodules and rare plant fragments, crop out below the lower leaf of the Rivelin Grit. The shales, which have yielded rare specimens of *Gastrioceras* crop out *in situ* as well as forming part of a slumped area (recognized by the hummocky ground) below the crags of the Rivelin Grit. Continue examining the shale outcrops up the slope towards the crags and note that they coarsen slightly until, just below the grit, the shales are interbedded with thin cross-laminated siltstone and fine sandstones. The lower leaf of the Rivelin Grit rests with a sharp junction (scoured surface) on the interbedded siltstones and sandstones. The grit is formed of apparently massive sandstones, but careful observation will reveal the presence of diffuse bedding and interbedded siltstone horizons. Further up the slope a poorly exposed interval indicates the presence of a finer-grained unit before further thick sandstones are exposed at the top of the slope. To reach Locality 8 at Upper Burbage Brook, return to the road and continue in a northerly direction (passing the car park) until Upper Burbage Bridge is reached. Descend to the exposures between the road and the confluence of the two streams.

Locality 8 (SK 261829). Here, on the top bedding surfaces of the small scarp, bedding planes of the sandstones show numerous, but poorly preserved and crudely aligned plant fragments (some as casts, others partly carbonized). From here, descend into Burbage Brook and follow the stream southwards. If the water level is low enough, very soon exposures of horizontally bedded carbonaceous siltstones and thinly bedded sandstones appear in the bed and banks of the stream. These beds occur below the upper leaf of the Rivelin Grit; the lower leaf being poorly exposed downstream. Intermittent exposures of shales are present along the length of the stream in the Burbage area. Marine fossils (*?Gastrioceras*) have been recorded at SK 262825 and some of the shale exposures show thin interbeds of ironstone.

Return to the car park by walking north along the stream, or head west or northwest (depending how far south you are in Burbage Brook) towards the southwestern end of the prominent scarp on the skyline. The road is close and it is a short distance to the car park.

Excursion 10b

Locality 1, Bradgate Brickyard (SK 413935). The quarry is located to the right of the road at the top of a grassy bank, just after crossing over the roundabout with the junction of the A629. The quarry face may be in variable states of degradation but most of the features described below should be exposed. The gentle northeast dip (Fig. 10.3b) is clearly visible, as is the range of rock types that make up typical Coal Measure cycles. Shales and mudstones with ironstone nodules, in which comminuted plant debris is locally abundant, dominate the sequence. Thin coal seams, seatearths and variably developed siltstones and fine-grained sandstones also occur. The mudrocks are dominantly non-marine but show evidence of occasional marine incursions; the siltstones and sandstones are the result of mainly fluvial activity, while the coals and seatearths indicate plant colonization during periods of emergence.

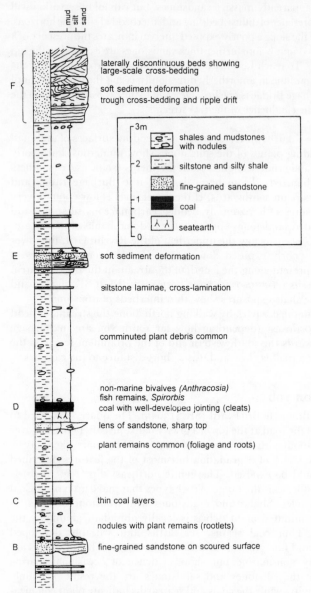

Figure 10.3 (a) Simplified sedimentary log of the sequence exposed in Bradgate Brickyard quarry.

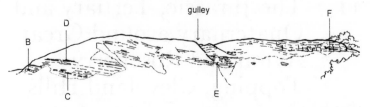

Figure 10.3 (b) Field sketch of the sequence exposed in Bradgate Brickyard quarry.

Point **A** (not shown on Fig. 10.3) is the level of the Joan Coal and overlying shales; these are usually obscured by scree. The Joan Coal lies approximately 14 m below the sandstone bed at **B**. The dark grey shales immediately above the coal have yielded the inarticulate **brachiopod** *Lingula* (horizon equivalent to Clay Cross Marine Band in this area). The geological features within the 15 m of strata exposed in the quarry may be followed on the log (Fig. 10.3a) with reference to the four prominent beds or units **B–F**. Point **G** (not shown on Fig. 10.3) is the level of the Lidgett Coal (rarely exposed) which occurs approximately 5.5 m above the top of the sandstones at **F**. Thin coal seams are present between the sandstones at **F** and the Lidgett Coal.

Please keep any disturbance of the rock face to a minimum.

11 · The Jurassic, Tertiary and Quaternary around Great Ayton and Roseberry Topping, Cleveland Hills

John Senior *University of Durham* and
Jim Rose *Royal Holloway, University of London*

PURPOSE

To examine the Lower and Middle Jurassic sedimentary succession and the Tertiary Cleveland **Dyke** intrusion in the area around Great Ayton and Roseberry Topping; to investigate how this rock sequence, together with the late Quaternary glaciation of the area, controls the form of the landscape.

LOGISTICS

This is a gentle full-day excursion covering 12.5 km. Numerous recognized paths and bridleways allow the route to be easily altered, shortened, lengthened or taken in reverse order. Park in Great Ayton, near the Tourist Information Office (NZ 563107), or at the Gribdale Gate car park (NZ 593110), which is usually used for visits to the Cook Monument. Theft from cars is a serious risk at more remote sites. If travelling by train, Great Ayton station (NZ 575108) is on the line from Middlesbrough, via Nunthorpe and the Esk valley, to Whitby. There are toilets, cafes and pubs in Great Ayton, but no other facilities en route.

Maps

O.S. 1:50 000 Sheet 93, Middlesbrough & Darlington; O.S. 1:25 000 Outdoor Leisure Sheet 26, North York Moors, Western Area (preferred); B.G.S. 1:63 360 Sheet 34, Guisborough.

GEOLOGICAL AND GEOMORPHOLOGICAL BACKGROUND

The area is on the western edge of the steep Cleveland Hills escarpment (Cleveland: in the Orkneyinga Saga *Klifland* or *Clifa-land* 'district of cliffs'), a classic piece of escarpment country with steep north- and west-facing slopes composed of softer Lower Jurassic rocks (in part Liassic shales) capped by more resistant Middle Jurassic sandstones. Roseberry Topping, a prominent landmark throughout the Cleveland Basin, is an erosional **outlier**, where the Middle Jurassic sandstone (Ravenscar Group) is detached from the main plateau. This Lower to Middle Jurassic sedimentary succession **dips** gently towards the south-southeast. Where the sandstones form the parent materials, acid soils characterize the upland plateaux, producing the heather moorland that is so characteristic of the North York Moors.

Although the Liassic sediments on the scarp slope are generally softer shales, the Middle Lias does include two more durable rock formations: the Staithes Formation and the Cleveland Ironstone Formation. Both form minor bench-like features and escarpments on the scarp slopes.

The intrusion of the Cleveland Dyke some 59 **Ma** ago has had a strong influence on the local landscape. This hard **tholeiitic** dyke (part of the dyke swarm from the Mull volcanic centre) forms the core of the west-northwest trending Langbaugh Ridge, visible from Great Ayton and Roseberry Topping. A local source of road metal, this dyke has been extensively quarried in the past 100 years or so. The dyke is about 25 m wide near Great Ayton and seems to have been regionally injected as a series of *en echelon* segments. In the Cliff Ridge Quarry near Great Ayton there is some evidence that the dyke was injected in leaves, separated by sediment screens; the Liassic dyke wall rocks have undergone incipient contact **metamorphism**.

Evidence for glaciation in the region takes the form of **tills, glaciofluvial** sands and gravels and **lacustrine** silts and clays on the lower slopes and in the valley bottoms. Additionally, glacial **meltwater channels**, located in anomalous positions without a drainage catchment, have been recognized and used as evidence to determine the slope of the glacier surface and the pattern of ice wastage. This evidence is attributed to the Dimlington **Stadial** of the Late Devensian Glaciation, when glaciers extended southward in eastern England to the region of the Wash, reaching their maximal extent about 17 000 ^{14}C yrs BP. Ice probably melted from the region sometime between about 16–15 000 ^{14}C yrs BP (Catt in Ehlers & Rose, 1991). This ice failed to cover the higher parts of the Cleveland Hills, but was responsible for infilling the valley bottoms, reducing the relative relief of the region and significantly changing the valley bottom topography, producing many buried valleys throughout northeast England.

Although not glacierized during the Dimlington Stadial it is probable that the higher slopes were overridden by ice at some time earlier in the Quaternary, as resistant **erratic** pebbles have been recorded from the plateau surfaces of the Cleveland Hills. There is, as yet, no evidence to estimate the age of this earlier glaciation(s).

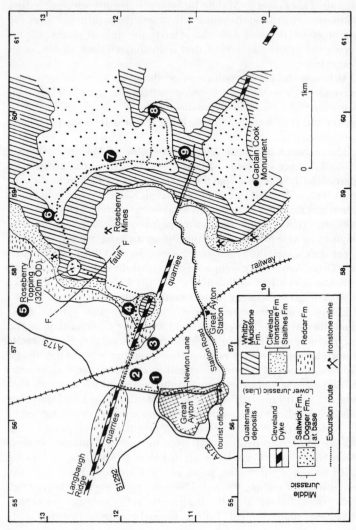

Figure 11.1 Geological map of the area around Great Ayton and Roseberry Topping, showing the route.

People have had a long-term influence on the landscape in this part of the Cleveland Hills. Mesolithic, Neolithic, Bronze and Iron Age peoples settled the region, helping to create the present-day 'grouse moor' landscape of the upland areas by forest clearance. Their presence is evidenced by well-defined ridge routes as well as numerous defensive sites, enclosures, field patterns, clearance cairns and burial tumuli. Monastic sheep farming created grange communities with associated field holdings, and medival iron smelting using local iron ores also added to the wealth of the Abbey or Priory. Sedimentary iron ore extraction (from the Cleveland Ironstone Formation) in the 19th century, by opencast and deep mine methods, has left a visible legacy of industrial archaeology. Large-scale Alum Shale workings have also left their mark on the Cleveland Hills landscape. Jet mining from the Upper Lias Shales (Mulgrave Shale Member) in the 19th century was more localized but the extraction bell pits can still be seen.

EXCURSION DETAILS

From the Tourist Information Centre, Great Ayton (NZ 563107), walk northwards along Newton Road. Note that the older properties in the village are built of a fine-quality reddish-brown sandstone with characteristic worked chevron tooling. One of the sources for this Middle Jurassic building stone can be visited at Locality 8. Also note the Tile Yard Pub, an indication that pan tiles were locally manufactured from glacial lake clays.

Locality 1 (NZ 563114), at the junction with the A173. Look north to the very evident Langbaugh Ridge, the core of which is the Tertiary Cleveland Dyke. Differential erosion of the softer Lower Liassic sediments from around this dyke has resulted in this prominent feature which stretches west-northwest into the Tees Basin. Tills mask the bedrock on either side of the ridge. Langbaugh Ridge has been extensively quarried for roadstone (NZ 555123–564120). Continue up the A173 to the summit of the ridge and take the bridle road east-southeast towards Cliff Ridge Wood and Roseberry Topping.

Locality 2 (NZ 566119). Just before crossing the railway bridge, stop to contemplate the magnificent view of Roseberry Topping to the northeast (Fig. 11.2). The stepped profile of this Teesside landmark is easy to interpret, with the more resistant parts of the Jurassic succession (chiefly sandstones and ironstones) producing the cap rock and scarp edge bench features. The cliff to the south of the hill with the area of disturbed ground in front results from a spectacular rotational landslide, generated on Liassic shales with the feature accentuated by mining and stone quarrying. Continue into the deep roadstone workings in Cliff Ridge Wood.

Locality 3 (NZ 570118–576116). The deep ravines through this wooded ridge result from extensive extraction of the dyke rock for road metal. Large blocks of the tholeiite, containing large crystals (phenocrysts) of **feldspar** set in a fine-grained matrix, can still be seen scattered throughout the workings. In some areas of the south wall minor leaves of the dyke, with associated sediment screens, may still be viewed *in situ*. All the wall rocks of the dyke show incipient contact metamorphism and these more indurate sediments form the sheer walls and pinnacles. *(This locality can be dangerous, with sheer drops masked by trees and shrubs; there is also the danger of falling blocks from the wall areas.)*

The dyke has been intruded into Lower Jurassic sediments. Approaching from the west the first sediments encountered are the silty shales of the Ironstone Shales (Lower Pliensbachian; Upper Redcar Mudstone Formation). These shales with nodule horizons are characteristic of the upper part of the Lower Lias; they tend to be poorly fossiliferous but occasional **bivalves** and the characteristic **ammonite** *Androgynoceras* (*davoei* **Biozone**) may be found.

Eastwards, the sediments become more silty and eventually grade imperceptibly into the silts and sandstones of the shallower-water deposits of the Staithes Formation (Middle Lias; Upper Pliensbachian). It is difficult to view these sediments *in situ* as they often form the upper levels of the quarry ravines. However, numerous fallen blocks show these marine impure sandstones to be richly fossiliferous with common Middle Lias bivalves such as *Pseudopecten*, *Protocardia*, *Pseudolima*, *Liostrea* and *Pholadomya* as well as numerous **belemnites** and the **brachiopod** *Tetrarhynchia*. More rarely, the index ammonite *Amaltheus* might be found (*margaritatus* Biozone), and brittle stars. The fossils almost always occur as natural moulds as the rock has been decalcified.

Return westwards to the start of the ravine area and take a path to the right to join the public right of way through the woods to the north of the quarry area.

Locality 4 (NZ 572118). At the top of the hill are the remains of the winding house and incline for the mineral line from the Roseberry Ironstone Mines. Continue due east towards Airy Holme Farm (Airy = Norse/Irish for 'shieling', i.e. summer pasture residence) where a southeastward-sloping glacial drainage channel formed during the melting of the last ice sheet. Just before the first house, turn north-northwest up the marked right of way along the field boundary towards Roseberry Topping. Note the prominent bench feature between Roseberry Topping and Cliff Ridge Wood, formed by the sandstones of Middle Lias Staithes Formation (NZ 574121). Under favourable conditions the continuation of the mineral line may be seen diagonally cutting the field to your left, crossing the path at NZ 576119 and continuing to the east in a shallow cutting. Near here, erratic boulders, hand cleared from the fields, may be seen in heaps at the field boundaries. They include the distinctive Shap Granite from Cumbria, indicating ice flow from that region, across the Stainmore gap of the Pennines, to the lower Tees valley and Cleveland. Ultimately the ice moved southwards and across the eastern side of the Cleveland Hills and North York Moors.

Continuing northeast towards Roseberry Topping, the path (at about 230 m OD) starts to skirt the eastern edge of the landslip. Note the large and jumbled blocks of sandstone on the disturbed ground to the west. To the southeast are areas of vegetated abandoned quarries and isolated pits in the field nearby, where sedimentary ironstones of the Cleveland Ironstone Formation (Middle Lias) have been extracted. The steep path towards the summit of Roseberry Topping crosses the horizon of the Mulgrave Shale Member (Whitby Mudstone Formation, Upper Lias), marked by small bell pits for jet in the heather to the east of the path. Occasionally small pieces of jet may be found in this vicinity.

At the head of the landslip the fine cliff formed of trough **cross-bedded** sandstone (Saltwick Formation; Middle Jurassic) may be examined by traversing westwards from the path. These massive beds, which include slump structures, intraformational **conglomerates** and ironstone **concretions,** are underlain in places by Middle Jurassic Roseberry Topping Plant Bed (channel fill deposits) containing the tree ferns *Nissonia*, *Ptilophyllum*, *Thinfeldia*, the cycad *Zamites* and stems of the horsetail *Equisetites*. These plant beds should not be damaged in any way.

Locality 5, Roseberry Topping (NZ 579126). On a clear day Roseberry Topping, capped by the Middle Jurassic sandstone outlier, affords fine views of the Eston Hills and Teesside to the north, the Cleveland Hills escarpment to the southwest, and Eskdale and the North York Moors to the southeast. The ridge formed by the Cleveland Dyke intrusion can be seen stretching out west-northwest into the Liassic

Figure 11.2 Roseberry Topping (Locality 5), viewed from the southwest. *Photo*: J. Senior.

and Triassic lowlands with their cover of glaciogenic sediments.

Walking east on the ridge path (Cleveland Way) between Roseberry Topping and Newton Moor you can see to the south uneven grassed terrain, the working areas (with remains of the mineral railway) associated with the Roseberry ironstone workings (NZ 584124). Some 2 km to the southeast, at the same geographical and geological level, is the even larger area of disturbed ground of the Ayton Banks Mines. Here the overlying Alum Shale Member (Whitby Mudstone Formation, Upper Lias) was also exploited as feed stock for alum production. The extensive exploitation of the sedimentary iron ores of the Cleveland Ironstone Formation (Middle Lias) in the area is witnessed by many mine **adits** and opencast workings.

Locality 6 (NZ 587128). Before the Cleveland Way reaches the edge of the escarpment it passes over a series of earthworks. Some of these are of recent origin – sandstone quarries for local walling. However one deeper excavation cutting north–south across the watershed may be a defensive ditch.

The route now follows the Cleveland Way southwards along the edge of the escarpment which is capped by deltaic sediments of the Middle Jurassic (Saltwick Formation). These sediments form a prominent feature, now largely masked by conifer plantations.

Locality 7 (NZ 593119). Here views may be had of the escarpment with a spring line at the junction between the sandstones and the underlying Upper Lias shales. A prominent quarry on the escarpment (NZ 589127) may have provided good quality building sandstone (from a discrete channel fill facies) for local buildings. The bulk of the Middle Jurassic sandstones capping the escarpment and dip slope of Newton and Great Ayton Moors are of poor quality, soft and thin-bedded with interleaves of clay. This is a classic area of modern grouse moor management, with strips of heather cover being burnt off in rotation to provide new heather growth for the grouse to eat. This technique of controlled burning often exposes evidence of occupation of these upland areas and the area to the east of the Cleveland Way along the ridge has numerous examples of burial monuments, field boundaries and enclosures, and cairn fields (piles of stone collected from field areas).

At the northern edge of High Intake Plantation the route may be varied. Continue directly to Locality 9 via the conspicuous group of three cist burial chambers with associated enclosures (NZ 595114), or take one of the many sheep tracks eastwards across the moor towards the quarry complex marked on the O.S. map (Locality 8). A well-trodden path follows the valley side between the Great Ayton Moor and the quarry.

Locality 8 (NZ 600115). The quarry here is large and has been worked as a source of good building sandstone from one of the Middle Jurassic channel infills (Saltwick Formation). The importance of this quarry is in its superb illustration of quarrying methods and stone dressing (possibly 18th and 19th century). Only the thick beds (3–6 m) of best-quality stone have been worked; the overburden of poor-quality, inter-channel, soft, silty sandstones with coal lenses having been ignored or scraped off. The massive sandstones (cross-bedded in places) seem to have been worked without the use of explosives, and many of the remaining working faces show extensive tool marks produced when levering out the blocks. This quarry seems to have been abandoned in production and many half-dressed blocks of ashlar can be seen, with the possible remains of stone-based working tables (bankers). The dressed ashlar blocks have the characteristic chevron finish as seen in Great Ayton and elsewhere in Cleveland and the North York Moors. Fine views of Lonsdale and the Esk valley may be had from the quarry top.

Leave the quarry by the rutted trackways that skirt the hill to the southwest. Pass by a very large Iron Age ditched rectangular enclosure and a smaller enclosure nearby (NZ 599133). This pathway also passes a smaller sandstone quarry at NZ 595112 (other sandstone quarries may be seen above the car park at NZ 592111 and NZ 591109).

Locality 9 (NZ 594112–594111). Where this minor track reaches the well-developed track near a small beck, follow the stream bed downhill. In the stream section thin-bedded sandstones of Middle Jurassic age are underlain by a thick sequence of shales. Some disturbed ground on this junction together with loose blocks of ironstone suggest that the Dogger Formation (Aalenian, Middle Jurassic) may have been worked by opencast methods at this locality. Occasional finds of *Dactylioceras commune* in the shale sequence at NZ 594111 indicate the presence of the Alum Shale Member (Whitby Mudstone Formation; Upper Lias).

The track then passes through the col known as Gribdale Gate (NZ 592110) which is believed to have been used by meltwater drainage during the wastage of the last ice sheet, and may have been formed by meltwater erosion at an earlier time in the Quaternary. Join the road near the car park (NZ 583110). Note that the tracks from the sandstone quarries head towards Great Ayton. A gentle downhill road leads back to the station or Great Ayton, with views of the Ayton Bank iron mines and Alum Shales workings on your left.

12 · The Quaternary features of Scugdale, northwest Cleveland Hills

Donald Frost *British Geological Survey, Newcastle upon Tyne*

PURPOSE

To examine the Quaternary landforms and deposits of Scugdale and around Swainby on the northwest corner of the Cleveland Hills.

LOGISTICS

The excursion involves a total of about 7 km of easy walking.

Maps

O.S. 1:50 000 sheets 93 Middlesbrough & Darlington, 99 Northallerton & Ripon, and 100 Malton & Pickering; 1:23 000 Outdoor Leisure Map, North York Moors (NW & SW Sheets); 1:63 360 Tourist Map of the North York Moors; B.G.S. 1:50 000 Sheet 42 Northallerton.

GEOLOGICAL BACKGROUND

Most of the York and Teesside plains are covered by **drift** deposits of Devensian age (Dimlington **Stadial** – 26 000 to 13 000 BP). The glacial deposits are the product of an ice-sheet which spread southwards about 18 000 years ago and subsequently began to melt about 13 000 years ago. Older (pre-Devensian) deposits may be present in buried valleys and more recent Flandrian sediments locally overlie the Devensian deposits and modify the glacial topography.

The powerful early ice-sheets streamed out eastwards and southeastwards from the Lake District and southwest Scotland, being joined en route by less powerful ice from local Pennine glaciers occupying Wensleydale and Swaledale. Much of the ice came through the Stainmore Gap, with part continuing eastwards down the Tees, and another branch swinging south through the Vale of Mowbray into the York Plain. The total thickness of ice in the central Tees lowlands was probably about 800 m. As the ice-sheet melted and retreated from the Cleveland Hills, both downhill and northwards, it left behind a complex sequence of glacial deposits including **till** (boulder clay), sand and gravel, laminated clay, lacustrine clay, silt, sand and **loess.** Such lithologies also form distinctive morphologies indicative of their origin, **drumlins, eskers**, sites of glacial lakes and **meltwater channels**. There are no well-preserved **moraines** in this area comparable with the York and Eskrick features further south. However the margins of the hills around Scugdale abound with meltwater channels. This excursion highlights these features in the Osmotherley–Swainby area (Fig. 12.1).

EXCURSION DETAILS

Locality 1, Scarth Nick Meltwater Channel. The excursion begins from a car park (SE 471993) on the minor road at the northern end of the Osmotherley (Cod Beck) Reservoir. Take this road to the north, which here occupies the bottom of the meltwater channel. Its sides are over 30 m high, and the base, at an altitude of about 220 m, is floored by peat. The gradient is largely to the south but a section drained north for a short period. At the northern end of Scarth Nick, sandstone crags are exposed and form the eastern side of the feature. Well-developed joints aligned parallel with the channel are indicative of a nearby **fault** which occupies the centre of the channel and was a contributory factor in the formation of this valley.

The meltwater channel follows the present line of the Cod Beck Valley southwards. Similar channels further south in the proximity of Nun House (SE 446940) at an altitude of about 150 m may represent the continuation of this marginal flow around the western edge of the Cleveland Hills. Confirmation that a 'lakelet' occupied the Cod Beck Valley for a short period during the Devensian is now provided by boreholes sunk along the dam line of the reservoir which proved it is filled by up to 8 m of laminated clays and silts and interlaminated sands. Below the dam, at the caravan site, a borehole (SE 46149808) proved silty clay and gravel to a depth of 27 m.

On the western flank of Scarth Nick, two small patches of gravel (NZ 470000) occur at an altitude of some 260 m. They are rich in **chert** and sandstone pebbles and form the remnants of a **glacio-fluvial** deposit associated with the meltwater channel.

Locality 2, Holy Well Gill Meltwater Channel. From the eastern side of Scarth Nick follow the southern edge of the forest eastwards around

Limekiln Bank to a good vantage point about 3 km from the road (SE 488996). Here the forest ends, giving an uninterrupted view of Scugdale. The valley was once filled by ice. The subsequent meltwater was dammed up by the remaining plug of ice across the mouth of Scugdale which not only faced north but lay in the shadow of the northerly scarp of the Cleveland Hills. The first areas to melt would have been on the south-facing flanks of Live Moor (NZ 504011). Stony

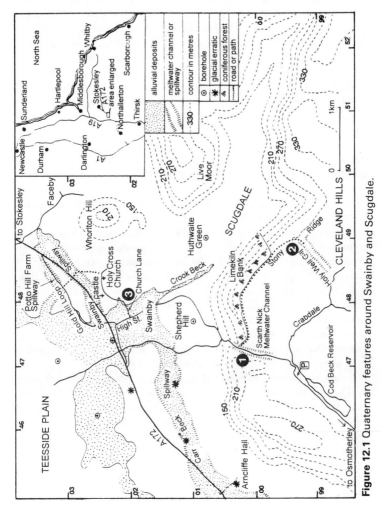

Figure 12.1 Quaternary features around Swainby and Scugdale.

Ridge on the southwest side probably acted as a solid rock rim to 'Lake Scugdale'. Eventually a notch was eroded at one point (SE 490992) along this ridge and an impressive glacial drainage channel was cut which now has the name Holy Well Gill. The Gill is dry and eroded into brown, fine-grained, ferruginous sandstone of the mid-Jurassic Ravenscar Group (Crinoid Grit Member). It is some 10 m deep and between 2 and 4 m wide. This channel is the highest recorded in the Cleveland area but its duration as a water-bearing channel was probably short-lived. The water drained into Crabdale and no doubt collected in the Cod Beck Valley, forming a 'lakelet' which eventually drained through the lower channel of Scarth Nick. A small patch of sand and gravel (SE 488996) on the northern side of Holy Well Gill at an altitude of about 305 m is possibly a remnant of a morainic ridge or reworked glaciofluvial beach deposit marginal to 'Lake Scugdale'.

The Holy Well Gill channel can be followed down into Crabdale to return to the Osmotherley Reservoir car park, or walk back along Stony Ridge and Limekiln Bank to the road.

Locality 3, Swainby Moraine and Glacial '**Spillways**'. Travel by car northwards through Scarth Nick and down the steep northern edge of the Cleveland Hills, taking the right fork for Swainby some 3 km distant. Ample parking is available near the village church on the corner of High Street and Church Lane.

The lower ground at the foot of the Cleveland Scarp shows typical hummock topography attributed to the outwash and morainic debris resulting from the melting of the ice damming 'Lake Scugdale'. A borehole (NZ 47710100) near Shepherd Hill proved glacial deposits to a depth of at least 25 m. They comprised mostly yellow-brown clays with sand lenses in the upper 7 m, which overlie clayey sand and gravel in the lower section of the borehole. The sand becomes increasingly clayey towards the base. Another borehole at Huthwaite Green (NZ 49010081) on the opposite side of Scugdale proved yellow-brown stony till to a depth of at least 8 m.

Swainby is sited on a broad alluvial flat, in places up to 1 km wide, and out of all proportion to the size of the existing Crook Beck and Scugdale Beck which drain northwards through the village along the edge of High Street. The following glacial and post-glacial features were formed towards the end of the Devensian when the waning ice-sheet was largely confined to the lowland areas of the Teesside plain.

The area is rich in glacial spillways. They comprise flat-bottomed channels, 10 to 30 m wide, but with sharply defined edges of variable height. They may have been cut by sub-glacial streams or represent periods of still-stand in the ice as it retreated northwards. The water became restricted to these channels, confined by the emerging scarp of the Cleveland Hills to the south and the ice-front to the north. Boreholes in the bottom of the spillways show the top 4 m or so to comprise recent alluvial deposits of soft grey mottled yellow clays and peat, overlying more than 14 m of brown clays with weak inter-laminations of silt and fine sand. A 0.10 m sample of peat (NZ 45250081) in the alluvium of Carr Beck, near Ingleby Arncliffe, was radiometrically **dated** at between 6450 ± 40 ^{14}C yrs BP. The locality is described as a 'gutter' on the inner edge of the Scugdale Moraine, attributed to glaciofluvial erosion, and its final silting-up is therefore datable to the Atlantic Period.

Walk up Church Lane on the east side of Swainby High Street and climb Castle Bank to the remains of Whorlton Castle. The site utilized the steep bank of the Swainby glacial channel as its main defence to the north in medieval times. The bank is now subject to several small landslips in the drift and underlying shales of the basal beds of the early Jurassic Redcar Mudstone Formation. From this vantage point, the Swainby and Carr Beck spillway, which formed a major avenue for meltwater around the northwest corner of the Cleveland Hills, is clearly seen.

Walk to the Holy Cross Church where Roman pottery has been discovered and take the path north where the road turns at right angles. Follow the path down across the channel and the main A172 Stokesley road to Potto Hill Farm (NZ 48050309). From here another spillway can be viewed parallel with the Swainby spillway in its easterly section. It unites with the Swainby spillway near Gorselands (NZ 486034). However at Potto Hill Farm it swings northwestwards, eventually joining the alluvium of Potto Beck. Turn left at Potto Hill Farm and walk westwards on the Gold Hill loop road which enables a 2 km circular return to Swainby.

The Swainby area contains many glacial **erratics**. The most striking are those derived from the Shap Granite in Cumbria. Large examples, up to 1 m in length, are present at locations NZ 46750128, NZ 45870114 and adjacent to the main road at NZ 46630199. A **basaltic** erratic occurs near Arncliffe All Saints Church (NZ 45230031), derived from either the Whin **Sill** or the Cleveland **Dyke**.

13 · The Permian and Carboniferous rocks of Knaresborough

Anthony Cooper *British Geological Survey, Newcastle upon Tyne*

PURPOSE

This day-long excursion visits Knaresborough Gorge, a glacial diversion channel. It examines the Permian strata and their **unconformable** relationship to the underlying Carboniferous rocks.

LOGISTICS

If the complete excursion is to be undertaken an entrance fee (which includes car parking) is payable to do the 'Long Walk' and visit Mother Shipton's Cave (telephone (0423) 864600 for details of charges). Permission to visit Bunker's Hill Quarry (Locality 3) must be sought in advance from Mrs B. Raistrick (tel. 0423 866264). The starting point is Old Mother Shipton's (SE 345571), off the A59, just south of the River Nidd. Alternatively this section west of the river may be omitted and one of the Council-run public car parks (SE 345572 and SE 348567) used as a starting point. In this case Localities 1 and 2 are missed out and the section between High Bridge and Low Bridge on the east bank of the river is walked twice. Alternatively, a deviation can be made to the town and castle. The circular walk is fairly level, about 8 km long and passes numerous pubs, cafes, picnic places and public conveniences.

Hammers must not be taken on this excursion as it is not permitted to hammer any of the rock exposures.

Maps

O.S. 1:50 000 Sheet 104 Leeds, Bradford & Harrogate; 1:25 000 SE 35 Harrogate; B.G.S. 1:50 000 Sheet 62, Harrogate, Solid and Drift editions.

Geological Survey Memoir, Harrogate (Cooper & Burgess, in press).

GEOLOGICAL BACKGROUND

At the start of the last glacial advance (Devensian) the topography of the Knaresborough district was different to that seen today. The proto River Nidd ran to the north and east of the present town. It deviated from its present course at Nidd (SE 302608) and ran through Brearton and past Farnham (SE 345605) to the northern outskirts of Knaresborough (SE 363580), before heading eastwards. During the advance of the Devensian ice-sheet a thick fan of sand and gravel was deposited in this valley, emanating from the front of the ice-sheet via glacial channels around Farnham (SE 352606) and Occaney (SE 352619); this deposit is currently worked in the gravel pits north of Knaresborough (SE 356587). If Knaresborough is approached from the north via the B6166 from Boroughbridge the extent of this buried valley, and its associated sand and gravel deposits, can be appreciated from the road. As the ice advanced further to the south and west it over-rode the sand and gravel, completely blocking the proto-Nidd drainage and diverting the river westwards. Here the river exploited the lowest, softest rocks and incised the present Nidd Gorge. West of the Nidd Gorge the glacial deposits are generally thin and probably pre-Devensian in age; east of the gorge the Devensian deposits comprise thick hummocky glacial **till** with **moraines, eskers** and late glacial lake deposits.

The solid rocks exposed in Knaresborough Gorge are of Carboniferous (Namurian) and Upper Permian age. Here the Permian strata **overlap** onto and submerge a surface of irregular relief eroded in the underlying Carboniferous sandstones and shales. The exposed Carboniferous sequence extends upwards from the Lower Follifoot Grit to the Upper Plompton Grit. At the northern end of Knaresborough the Carboniferous rocks are folded around the nose of the Harrogate **Anticline** and **dip** at up to 27° to the east and southeast. This anticline was formed during the **Variscan Orogeny,** prior to the late Permian deposition.

The overlying Permian strata dip gently eastwards and rest unconformably on the Carboniferous rocks (cross-section in Fig. 13.1). The lowest Permian rocks seen here are the Cadeby Formation (formerly Lower Magnesian Limestone). This formation is over 40 m thick and subdivided into two members: the Wetherby Member (formerly Lower Subdivision) and the Sprotbrough Member (formerly Upper Subdivision). The Cadeby Formation (Sprotbrough Member) forms the ridge on which Knaresborough is built. The ridge consists largely of **cross-bedded oolites** and is capped by a small

outlier of Edlington Formation (formerly Middle Marl). The Knaresborough ridge appears to be a primary depositional feature, for the limestone thins away from it in all directions and depositional dips mimic the form of the ridge. The thinning of the formation is best illustrated northwest of the town centre, near Conyngham Hall, where it thins to 1–3 m of even-bedded, sandy **dolomite**; the westward thinning is illustrated by the cross-section in Fig. 13.1. The overlying Edlington Formation comprises red-brown calcareous mudstone with some **gypsum** and is generally poorly exposed. It overlaps the Cadeby Formation both northwards and westwards to rest directly on the Carboniferous rocks. The Edlington Formation is in turn overlapped by the Brotherton Formation (formerly Upper Magnesian Limestone), a sequence of dolomitic limestone 5–15 m thick, which rests directly on Carboniferous rocks at Scriven (SE 345585) and Rudfarlington (SE 342543).

EXCURSION DETAILS

Locality 1 (SE 34755685). Starting at Old Mother Shipton's car park, take the Long Walk to the Weir (SE 34755685); here Carboniferous sandstone (Addlethorpe Grit) is present in the river, and the sub-Permian unconformity is visible in the cliffs below the Walk. About 12 m of dolomite are exposed, overlain by red siltstones of the Edlington Formation. On the opposite bank of the river the Addlethorpe Grit and overlying Cadeby Formation form a sheer cliff; the unconformity at the base of the Permian sequence is clearly visible.

Locality 2 (SE 348565). Proceed southwards to the Dropping Well. Here there are several magnificent **tufa** screens produced by the carbonate- and sulphate-rich waters of the spring. The Dropping Well spring emanates from the dolomite of the Cadeby Formation, but includes dissolved sulphates derived from the gypsum of the overlying Edlington Formation. The carbonate is readily deposited from the water forming the Dropping Well screens and petrifying objects placed in its path. Mother Shipton's Cave, just north of the Dropping Well, is situated below an ancient tufa screen. Tradition says that the notorious sibyl of the North, Mother Shipton, was born near this well in the year 1488. Leave Old Mother Shipton's by the exit at Low Bridge, cross to the east side of the river and walk south about 50 m.

Locality 3 (SE 351565). At the entrance to Bunker's Hill Quarry (Caravan Park) massive, cross-bedded oolites of the Cadeby Forma-

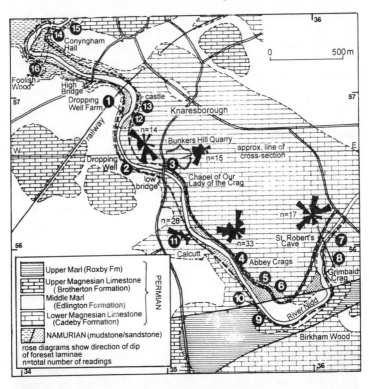

Figure 13.1 Geological map and cross-section of the Knaresborough area (with palaeocurrent information from Dr J. G. Kaldi).

tion are exposed in the cliff along to the House in the Rock and the Chapel of Our Lady of the Crag which may be visited upon payment of an entrance fee. The chapel was formerly known as St Robert's Chapel after the monk who built it (see Locality 7 for further details). To visit the rock faces in Bunker's Hill Quarry (SE 35155655) permission must be sought in advance from the caravan site owner (see Logistics). Near the Chapel of Our Lady of the Crag the cliffs show rows of post holes from the roofs of houses occupied by weavers up to about 1840. Hereabouts the rock faces show sections of oolitic dolomite which occurs in massive cross-bedded units with sets up to 18 m high; these belong to the Sprotbrough Member of the Cadeby Formation. These units represent massive subaqueous oolite sand waves. There is general westward thinning of the sequence from here to Callcut (see cross-section in Fig. 13.1).

Locality 4 (SE 355559). Proceed southwards along the road to the south end of the garden of the last house (Amtree House) on the east of the road. Please keep out of the private garden. At the far entrance to the grounds, looking up at the rock face to the east, the unconformity between the massive sand-wave facies of the Cadeby Formation and the underlying Upper Plompton Grit is exposed, now sadly overgrown and best seen in winter. The sandstone is reddened and takes the form of a rounded buried hill with an exposed relief of 8 m and a width of 32 m (Fig. 13.2). The overlying Cadeby Formation covers the buried hill with subconcentric drapes of beds 0.1–0.15 m thick. On its flanks they pass laterally into large-scale (1–10 m) cross-bedding. The Cadeby Formation here comprises fine-grained crystalline to granular dolomite with sporadic poorly preserved ooliths.

Figure 13.2 Carboniferous-Permian unconformity at Abbey Crags (Locality 4). *Photo*: B.G.S.

Locality 5 (SE 357557). Continue southwards to the car turning point. Northeast of here the unconformity at the base of the Cadeby Formation dips down into a buried valley, but reappears in the quarry east of the road. Here 3.6 m of Carboniferous sandstone (Upper Plompton Grit) is present beneath 13.5 m of Cadeby Formation. The reddened and weathered sandstone is very coarse to granule-grained, **feldspathic**, with **quartz** pebbles, and occurs in very thick cross-bedded units. At the base of the overlying limestone there is a thin impersistent bed (0–0.1 m) of yellow, very coarse-grained sandstone with a dolomitic cement. It is not apparent whether this is part of the Carboniferous sequence, re-cemented with dolomite, or a very sandy bed at the base of the Permian. The overlying thin, medium and thick beds comprise dolomite with quartz grains in the lowest 0.5 m or so.

Locality 6 (SE 357557). About 100 m southeast of Locality 5 the same unconformity rises to the top of the old quarry in the private grounds east of the road, from where it can be well seen. The quarry should not be entered. The section now exposes 10.5 m of Carboniferous sandstone overlain by 4 m of dolomite. This shows that locally the relief on the unconformity is at least 8 m.

Locality 7 (SE 361570). Continue along the riverside road to the north-northeast for about 500 m where St Robert's Cave is situated in the river bank below the road; entry is through a gap in the wall and down a flight of steps. This cave was the former abode of the pious monk Robert Flower of York from Fountains Abbey, AD 1160–1218. He took refuge in the cave and turned another cave into St Robert's Chapel (Locality 3). The cave also gained notoriety as the scene in 1745 of the murder of Daniel Clark, for which crime Eugene Aram, a scholar of considerable ability, was hanged at York in 1759. At St Robert's Cave thin sub-horizontal beds of cross-bedded, oolitic dolomite are exposed with a channel structure to the south of the cave entrance. These beds are sparsely fossiliferous and probably represent the Wetherby Member (lower subdivision) of the Cadeby Formation. The member must, however, wedge out rapidly southwards because it is not present at Grimbald Crag (Locality 8) only 300 m to the south. From St Robert's Cave proceed northwards along the road, cross the River Nidd by the Wetherby Road, and head southwards on the riverside footpath to Grimbald Crag.

Locality 8 (SE 361558). Grimbald Crag exposes a sequence similiar to that found at Abbey Crags and reveals another hill in the pre-Permian topography. About 16 m of massive, cross-bedded dolomite rest unconformably on reddened Lower Plompton Grit with one footpath running along the unconformity. The unconformity was formerly exposed overlain by about 2 m of evenly bedded dolomitic limestone; then by massive cross-bedded units typical of the area (Dr D. B. Smith, pers. comm.). The unconformity is now obscured, but the lowest Permian beds seen contain abundant derived quartz grains. South of Grimbald Crag a **fault**, **downthrowing** to the south, brings the Brotherton Formation limestone outcrop against that of the Lower Plompton Grit.

Locality 9 (SE 35675552). The Brotherton Formation limestone is best seen at the top of the bank west of Birkham Wood. This exposure comprises 1.5 m of white and pale grey, thin-bedded, porcellanous, dolomitic limestone which contains fossils. These include small tube-like **algal** threads of *Calcinema permiana* which commonly occur in drifts and other concentrations, as well as the **bivalves** *Schizodus obscurus* and *Liebea*.

Locality 10 (SE 356556). About 100 m north of Locality 9, the Grimbald Crag Fault crosses the River Nidd opposite the Priory and is marked by a prolific spring. At this locality the Brotherton Formation limestone and Roxby Formation (formerly called the Upper Marl) are thrown against the Cadeby Formation, the fault scarp forming a prominent feature which can be traced to the west.

Locality 11 (SE 352560). North of the Grimbald Crag Fault, Calcutt Cricket Ground occupies a quarry excavated in the Sprotbrough Member of the Cadeby Formation. East of the quarry the Lower Plompton Grit is exposed in the river bed, while to the south and north the Edlington Formation overlies the dolomite of the Cadeby Formation. East of the Nidd, beneath Knaresborough, the Cadeby Formation is thick and its top rises to 75 m O.D., but at Calcutt it is thin and the top only rises to 53 m. As the regional dip of the Permian rocks is to the east, the westward thinning of the Cadeby Formation at this point is clearly illustrated (see cross-section in Fig. 13.1). Proceed along the riverside path to Low Bridge, a convenient place to break for lunch with pubs and toilets nearby.

Locality 12 (SE 348569). Cross the river at Low Bridge and head northwards on the east side of the Nidd. Below the castle the cliff section near the Weir, seen earlier from the opposite bank of the river, exposes the unconformity at the base of the Cadeby Formation. The 27 m high vertical face is not accessible. At road level 2–3 m of weathered Addlethorpe Grit is exposed with a fossilized tree-trunk present below an overhang about 1 m above ground level. The remaining 27 m of the cliff comprises a basal zone 6–7 m thick of reddish-buff sandy dolomite overlain by about 17 m of dolomite in large-scale cross-bedded units.

Locality 13 (SE 349569). For the energetic, a walk up the cliff path, just north of Locality 12, to Knaresborough Castle affords an opportunity to examine the Cadeby Formation at close hand and to visit the castle. The castle was originally Norman, though all traces of that period have now disappeared; then, from 1371, it was a stronghold of the Duchy of Lancaster and used as a barracks. From the castle viewpoint the form of the Knaresborough Gorge glacial diversion channel can be appreciated; return to the riverside walk (via the town to High Bridge if you have already walked this section).

Locality 14 (SE 34255742). Continue upstream past the High Bridge to Conyngham Hall Farm, where the track crosses the river again. About 50 m to the east, in the wooded area below Conyngham Hall, the attenuated Cadeby Formation (only 1.2 m thick) is seen resting on weathered purple-brown Carboniferous siltstones, and overlain by the Edlington Formation. The exposed Edlington Formation comprises 2.6 m of red-brown mudstone and sandstone. It includes sandy and micaceous detritus derived from Carboniferous sandstones similar to those exposed 100 m to the east, where the Edlington Formation rests directly on Carboniferous strata. The north–south cross-section through here is similar to the east–west cross-section shown in Fig. 13.1.

Locality 15 (SE 342575). Near Conyngham Hall Farm the Upper Follifoot Grit crosses the river, forming the foundations of the bridge. The sandstone dips to the east at 27° and comprises some 7 m of fine to medium-grained sandstone with subordinate siltstone partings and a thick bed of siliceous **ganister** with rootlets near the middle of the unit. The Carboniferous rocks here, and at Locality 16, dip steeply eastwards around the nose of the Harrogate Anticline. The resistant sandstone units form small escarpments projecting above the general level of the sub-Permian unconformity, and the basal Permian sedimentary rocks are banked against them.

The Permian and Carboniferous rocks of Knaresborough

Locality 16 (SE 34135722). Follow the river southwards to Foolish Wood where in an old quarry the Upper Follifoot Grit dips southwest at 27°. At the back of the quarry, sub-horizontal dolomite, 0.5 m thick, of the Cadeby Formation rests with a basal **conglomerate** of local material on an irregular sandstone surface, and is overlain by red siltstone. The sandstone apparently formed a ridge on the sea-floor prior to the deposition of the Cadeby Formation. Only a few metres to the north of the quarry, where the dolomite rests on siltstones underlying the Upper Follifoot Grit it thickens to 3 m, forming an escarpment from which large blocks have slipped down to the river bank.

Continue southwards on the west side of the River Nidd to Old Mother Shipton's car park.

14 · The Permian rocks of south-central Yorkshire

Denys Smith *GEOPERM and University of Durham*

PURPOSE

To examine the Permian sequence at outcrop in south-central Yorkshire and to infer its depositional environments.

LOGISTICS

A one-day excursion that may be followed in either direction and takes a minimum of about 8 hours (including a 1 hour break and travel totalling about 32 km between stops). All the exposures are close to the road with parking nearby.

Maps

O.S. 1:50 000 Sheets 105 York, and 111 Sheffield & Doncaster; B.G.S. 1:50 000 Sheets 70 Leeds, 78 Wakefield, and 87 Barnsley.

GEOLOGICAL BACKGROUND

The route follows the relatively narrow north–south outcrop of the Magnesian Limestone close to the depositional **strike** and the A1 and A1(M) roads. The rocks to be seen (Table 14.1) are mainly of **dolomite** and comprise the carbonate units of cycles 1 and 3 of the English Zechstein (EZ) sequence (Smith *in* Rayner & Hemingway, 1974). All the statigraphical units thicken gradually eastwards and contain ovoid cavities up to 0.1 m across on the sites of former **anhydrite** patches.

The **unconformity**, seen at Locality 5, is a gently rolling mature peneplane with a low eastward slope and, in the excursion area, only a few minor eminences. It represents up to 35 **Ma** of sub-equatorial desert weathering during which the underlying Carboniferous rocks were uplifted, folded, **faulted**, reddened and eroded. Scattered

	Modern names	Old names		Thickness (m)
c				
a	Brotherton Formation	(Upper Magnesian Limestone)		13–18
—	Edlington Formation	(Middle Marls)		7–21
E	Cadeby Formation	(Lower Magnesian Limestone)	Sprotbrough Member	18–35
			Wetherby Member	15–25
r	Basal Permian (Yellow) Sands, patchy			0–6
e				
P	∼∼∼∼∼∼∼∼∼∼∼∼∼∼∼∼∼∼*unconformity* ∼∼∼∼∼∼∼∼∼∼∼∼∼∼∼∼∼∼∼			
	Upper Carboniferous Coal Measures			

Table 14.1 The Permian sequence in the excursion area.

angular pebbles of Coal Measures rocks litter this old land surface and wind-blown sand (subsequently redistributed during the ensuing marine transgression and seen at Locality 1) forms low sub-parallel ridges 2–8 km apart.

The long phase of desert conditions ended about 255 Ma ago when the area was rapidly flooded by the almost landlocked tropical Zechstein Sea in late Permian time, initiating about 5 Ma of intermittent marine **transgressions** and **regressions** as sea levels rose and fell and the floor of the Zechstein Basin gradually subsided. Shorelines extended as far west as the eastern slopes of the ancestral Pennines at times during Cycles EZ1 and EZ3, but receded eastwards by up to 50 km during phases of low sea level such as those during much of Cycle EZ2.

The scarp-forming lower (Wetherby) member, seen at Localities 1, 2, 3, 4, 5 and 7, is here almost entirely a shallow water to beach deposit that shows slight **onlap** against eminences on the flooded old land surface. It built up a basin-margin shelf of varied carbonate sediments (now dolomitized) including muds (Localities 1, 5), shelly **oolites** (Localities 2, 3, 4), shell banks or **coquinas** (Localities 2, 5) and patch-reefs (Localities 3, 4, 5). Cutting of the Hampole Discontinuity during a brief phase of slightly lower relative sea level initiated a relatively stable phase during which the Hampole Beds (Locality 7) were formed. This was then followed by a rapid re-inundation that led to the formation of the Sprotbrough Member; the crop of this lies so close to the depositional strike that all its exposures in the excursion area lie in a single **facies** belt, that of offshore large oolite sand waves (Locality 7).

Changes in the level of the sea or the sediment surface resulted in the main shoreline migrating far to the east near the end of Cycle EZ1 time and the Cadeby Formation was succeeded by the continental to

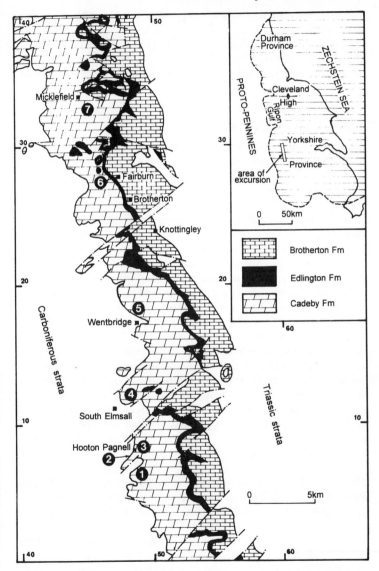

Figure 14.1 Geological map of Permian rocks in south-central Yorkshire (based on Geological Survey published maps). Inset shows approximate distribution of land and sea when the Cadeby Formation was being formed.

lagoonal muds, silts, sands and **evaporites** (mainly **gypsum** but with some **rock-salt**) of the Edlington Formation (not seen on this excursion). Further relative sea level change led to a widespread gentle re-transgression and the deposition of the partly dolomitized carbonate muds to sands of the shallow-water Brotherton Formation of Cycle EZ3 (Locality 6).

EXCURSION DETAILS

Locality 1 (SE 487066), part of former Bilham Sand Quarry S.S.S.I. (25 mins). Park in the gateway (48700672) opposite the sharp bend in the lane and walk 120 m to the southeast. This is a small conserved exposure straddling the contract of the Basal Permian (Yellow) Sands and the overlying Wetherby Member of the Cadeby Formation (Cycle EZ1). The Carboniferous/Permian unconformity was formerly exposed here but now lies 1–1.5 m below the quarry floor.

The Basal Permian Sands here are about 3.3 m thick (including the part now covered) and comprise almost level-bedded, yellow-brown, mainly medium-grained **arkosic** quartz sand with a patchy very weak carbonate cement; most of the grains are sub-angular to sub-rounded but some of the larger grains are rounded to well-rounded. The deposit is thought to have been a desert dune sand that was redistributed when the Zechstein Sea flooded the area.

The contact with the Wetherby Member here is smooth, sharp and almost horizontal and the exposed basal part of the Wetherby Member comprises about 3.5 m of thin-bedded buff finely crystalline dolomite; the lowest 0.8 m of this may be an altered oolite. The dolomite contains several films and thin beds of brown dolomitic clay and scattered, poorly preserved casts of small **bivalves**; it is interpreted as a marine deposit, formed under relatively shallow water of low to moderate energy.

Locality 2 (SE 483074), the old quarry in Second Plantation, Hooton Pagnell (20 mins). Park on the wide verge at the sharp corner of the lane and scramble 15 m to the north-northwest. This small quarry is cut into the escarpment of the Wetherby Member of the Cadeby Formation and supplied building stone. About 6 m of mainly thick-bedded buff shelly oolitic dolomite is exposed, the lowest beds lying an estimated 3–4 m above the unconformity (Basal Permian Sands being thin or absent). Some of the beds are so rich in shelly remains, mainly of the bivalves *Bakevellia*, *Liebea*, *Permophorus* and *Schizodus*, that they constitute coquinas and must have been shell-banks when they were formed. Where **joints** are widely spaced, these thick beds yielded blocks large enough to be used for window and door lintels and gate posts, all to be seen in and around nearby Hooton Pagnell village (Locality 3). Fully marine but very shallow-water and at least moderate energy conditions probably prevailed here when these sediments were accumulating.

Fields immediately southeast of Locality 2 comprise a **dip**-slope, which is cut by a southwest–northeast fault that **throws** up Coal Measures to the southeast and brings in a second Permian escarpment at Bilham Sand Quarry (Locality 1).

Locality 3 (SE 4808), Hooton Pagnell village (45 mins). There are several parking places, the largest just north of the church. *No hammers please!* This picturesque village, which has changed little for several centuries and featured in the Domesday Book, is built on solid rock in the scarp and crest of the Permian Escarpment. A leisurely stroll around the houses (but watch out for traffic in the narrow roads) reveals a host of small rock exposures, scarcely two the same, and close scrutiny of the locally derived shelly building stone and stone gateposts is particularly rewarding.

The rocks exposed are about 7 m thick, the lowest lying an estimated 3–4 m above the unconformity. They comprise a highly varied complex of small patch reefs, some compound, and surrounding shelly oolite. The reefs are roughly oval in cross-section and up to perhaps 40 m across; they mainly comprise buff finely crystalline dolomite arranged in a disorderly pile of sack-like masses ('sacco-liths') each typically 1–3 m across and 0.6 m thick, and contain a sparse framework of the small twig-like **bryozoan** *Acanthocladia* (an attached filter-feeder). The reefs interfinger with, and sharply abut against, the oolite which is generally similar to that seen at Locality 2 but is less shelly and contains, additionally, laminae and lenses of very finely crystalline dolomite (formerly carbonate mud) that fills shallow channels and drapes low-amplitude current ripples.

The most instructive building stones are in walls of buildings at the south end of the main street where a spectacular range of grains include **algal**-coated shell debris, algal-coated fragments of local Permian oolite up to 50 mm across, and almost infinitely varied ooliths, **pisoliths** and compound grains.

The exposures at Hooton Pagnell convey a vivid image of a shallow, white-floored tropical sea with scattered small sub-circular to elongate darker-coloured reefs rising less than a metre above the surrounding sea floor. These provided ecological niches for abundant small organisms that would not have survived in the current-swept exposed areas between and around the reefs.

Locality 4 (SE 483116), Field Lane Quarry S.S.S.I. South Elmsall (40 mins). Park at the roadside beside the quarry. *No hammers please; hard hats recommended.* This unique exposure of an almost complete cross-section of a patch-reef near the middle of the Wetherby Member of the Cadeby Formation is typical of reefs at this stratigraphical level and lies in bedded oolitic and pisolitic shelly dolomite. It comprises a core (C on Fig. 14.2) of massive dolomite with a densely packed but poorly preserved framework of small twiggy bryozoans (as at Hooton Pagnell), overlain by a mantle of conspicuously domed **stromatolites** (S on Fig. 14.2). The latter contain no shelly fossils but grade laterally into the surrounding bedded dolomite in which the remains of the bivalves *Bakevellia*, *Liebea* and *Schizodus* are locally abundant.

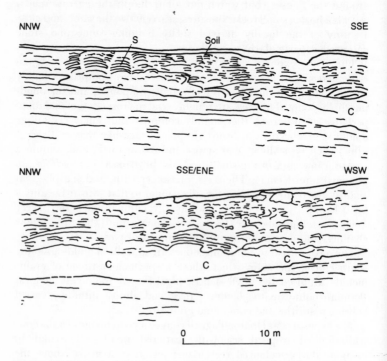

Figure 14.2 The bryozoan-stromatolite reef at South Elmsall.

The rocks exposed at South Elmsall, like those at Hooton Pagnell, were probably all formed in clear sea water no more than a few metres deep; there is no evidence of subaerial exposure or erosion.

A notice board gives additional information and interpretation.

Locality 5 (SE 487177), Wentbridge road cutting and quarry (45 mins). Park at the roadside, preferably on the west side north of the bend. The cutting is on the old A1 where it cuts through the escarpment of the Cadeby Formation; the scarp face here is particularly impressive, especially when viewed from the south of the River Went valley. The quarry is cut into the scarp in woodland on the east side of the road and some 70–100 m southeast of the cutting. Both cutting and quarry are somewhat overgrown in high summer, but well repay a little clearance.

The cutting exposes about 10 m of regularly bedded, partly **cross-bedded** oolitic dolomite of the Wetherby Member lying **disconformably** on Ackworth Rock sandstone of the early Upper Coal Measures. Some of the lower beds of the oolite contain many bivalves, especially *Bakevellia* and *Schizodus*.

The quarry exposes a typical bryozoan patch-reef lying in shelly oolitic dolomite as seen in the cutting. The reef is about 35 m across and 3 m thick and is formed of an untidy assemblage of sack-like masses, similar to those in the reefs at Locality 3; it abuts sharply against the surrounding oolites which contain very little reef-derived debris. A second, smaller, reef is also present and about 0.3 m of yellow-buff friable fine- to medium-grained sandstone beneath the oolite near the quarry entrance may be Basal Permian Sand.

The carbonate rocks at this locality were formed soon after the Zechstein Sea was created, probably under shallow clear sea water of normal salinity and moderate energy. The great abundance of bivalve casts near the base of the section is typical of the area and no reefs were formed before this shelly unit. The shells probably afforded a firm sea floor for the attachment of the reef-building bryozoans.

Locality 6 (SE 47132788), Fairburn village, two exposures at the foot of the high wall on the northeast side of the road and about 60–90 m northwest of The Three Horse Shoes public house (20 mins). There is parking almost opposite the exposure. *No hammering please.*

The Brotherton Formation (Cycle EZ3) is extremely uniform in this part of Yorkshire and where seen here is typical of much of the surrounding area except that it is dolomite. It comprises unevenly flaggy to thin-bedded finely crystalline buff dolomite with a variety of sedimentary structures (cross-lamination, ripples, cut and fill structures, etc.) that are suggestive of shallow-water accumulation. Some beds are graded, perhaps through being reworked during storms. Most beds are sparingly shelly but some are highly fossiliferous. Only two genera of bivalves – *Liebea* and *Schizodus* – are generally present, together with the 1 x 10 mm stick-like tubular remains of the supposed alga *Calcinema*. These remains, which occur locally in rock-forming proportions, commonly form aligned swarms on bedding planes. Salinity may have been slightly above normal and energy was generally low to moderate.

Limestone of the upper part of the Brotherton Formation was formerly widely worked in and around Brotherton, Ferrybridge and Knottingley but although quarrying has now almost ceased, hundreds of local walls and buildings testify to the vast amount of rock extracted and provide readily accessible examples of most of the rock-types present. The effects of differential subsidence caused by Tertiary or later dissolution of evaporites in the underlying Edlington Formation is seen in most of the quarry faces around Brotherton in the form of gentle sags, folds and minor faults.

There are many quarry faces of limestone of the Brotherton Formation east of the A1. For those with time to spare, or those travelling southwards, excellent exposures are to be found at Brotherton (SE 481267) and Knottingley (SE 498239).

Locality 7 (SE 446324), Micklefield Quarry S.S.S.I. (40 mins). Park in the quarry, behind the houses. *No hammering please; hard hats recommended.* An important section that exposes the Hampole Beds and adjoining parts of the Wetherby and Sprotbrough members of the Cadeby Formation (EZ1Ca) (see Table 14.2).

	Thickness (m)	
Pale cream finely oolitic dolomite with large-scale wedge-bedding; many burrows in places.	c.7.00+	Sprotbrough Mbr
Pale cream finely oolitic dolomite, medium-bedded at top, flaggy below.	c.0.65	
Hampole Beds Two thin beds of plastic grey-green dolomitic clay separated by 0.10–0.15 m of pale cream finely oolitic dolomite. In recess.	c.0.17	
Pale cream-buff unevenly microbially-layered oolitic dolomite with dense layers ("crusts"), rip-up **clasts** and a strong fenestral fabric. A single bed, clearly distinguishable from a distance.	c.0.80	Wetherby Mbr
Pale cream-buff oolitic dolomite, slightly unevenly thick-bedded, with some cross-bedding and cut and fill structures; scattered poor casts of bivalves and gastropods. Formerly seen to 4 m but now . . .	0.60+	

Table 14.2 The sequence at Micklefield Quarry.

The Hampole Beds record a phase when the sea level fell by a few metres and subsequently rapidly recovered. The sea level fall led to subaerial exposure and the cutting of the Hampole Discontinuity, an erosion surface that can be traced from Ripon to Nottingham, and the return of the sea caused the shoreline to retreat westwards. The area then became part of a north–south offshore belt of large white submarine sand waves composed of ooliths. The sediment below the sea floor at this time was able to support a variety of burrowing organisms but the current-swept sea floor itself was an inhospitable and dangerous place and few invertebrates survived to be preserved as fossils. The 'fenestral fabric' in the lower part of the Hampole Beds is thought to have been caused by the expansion of trapped methane bubbles given off by decaying organic (microbial) films ('algal mats') in the laminated intertidal sediment. The 0.8 m bed in which it is present is an excellent and readily recognizable building stone and features in most of the stone-built houses and walls in New Micklefield.

A notice board gives additional information and interpretation.

15 · Jurassic and Cretaceous rocks of the Market Weighton area

Felix Whitham *Treasurer, Hull Geological Society*

GEOLOGICAL SUCCESSION

The itinerary illustrates the late Cretaceous **chalk** succession and its basal **unconformity** on the Market Weighton Block. Surface features reflect erosion by meltwater along the main glacial **overflow channel** on the eastern side of the Yorkshire Wolds between Kiplingcotes and Market Weighton.

LOGISTICS

This one-day excursion can be divided into two half-days (Localities 1–5 and 6–8). Private transport is recommended, as there is no public transport from Market Weighton to the Kiplingcotes area. All exposures are accessible by road, with roadside parking available, and little walking is necessary. Most localities require permission for entry to be arranged in advance and contact details are given in the locality descriptions below.

Note: Safety helmets should be worn near quarry faces.

Maps

O.S. 1:50 000 Sheet 196 Market Weighton; O.S. 1:25 000 Sheet SE 84/94 Market Weighton; B.G.S. 1:63 360 Sheet 72 Beverley.

GEOLOGICAL BACKGROUND

Throughout Jurassic and early Cretaceous times, the area around Market Weighton was subjected to the intermittent uplift of the deep-seated Market Weighton Block. This structure, about 20 km across from north to south, trending east–west and continuing eastwards beyond the Holderness coast, separated slowly subsiding regions to the north and south. Its persistent buoyancy, associated with minor periods of erosion, resulted in a marked thinning or complete absence of sediments of Jurassic and early Cretaceous age across the Block (Kent, 1980).

In the Goodmanham area, almost all the Jurassic succession is absent. Thin remnants of Middle Lias resting on Lower Lias are overlain unconformably by attenuated early Cretaceous Albian deposits referred to the Carstone (under investigation) and Hunstanton Formation (Red Chalk). Early Cretaceous beds below the Carstone are absent between Market Weighton and north Lincolnshire, where they gradually reappear to the south. Late Cretaceous white chalk of the Ferriby, Welton and Burnham Formations **oversteps** the region with indications of thinning in the Cenomanian (Fig. 15.1). Near Rifle Butts Quarry (Fig. 15.2, Locality 1), a spring line indicates the base of the chalk.

The chalk of the area is generally harder than that of southern England, and in some sedimentary situations less pure chalks can be coloured red, pink or grey. **Flint** occurs commonly in the northern chalk succession with the exception of the lowest 30 m. The highest flints occur about 215 m above the base of the chalk at localities in the northeast of the region, where higher parts of the succession are seen. Vast sheets of thick, grey flint (tabular flint) and intermittent flat flints (lenticular flints) occur, mostly parallel to bedding, at a number of horizons within the chalk, some providing important marker horizons which can be traced throughout the Northern Province chalk. Nodular and burrow describe other forms of flint.

Marl bands occur frequently in the chalk. They contain **micro-** and **nannofossils** which can be used **biostratigraphically**. Some of these bands provide important marker horizons which can be correlated throughout the region.

A review of chalk exposures in the Kiplingcotes and Market Weighton area, together with recent new and temporary exposures, has made it possible to establish a more detailed local succession, 125 m thick, which extends from the basal Albian Hunstanton Formation up to the *Micraster cortestudinarium* Biozone of the Coniacian in the Burnham Formation (Fig. 15.1). A section created during the construction of the Market Weighton bypass (SE 895420 to 885910) exposed thin representatives of the Lower and Middle Lias, overlain by thin beds of Carstone (0.5 m) and Hunstanton Formation (1 m) and about 5 m of Lower Cenomanian chalk. The Lias beds yielded a fauna of **bivalves** and **ammonites,** whilst the **belemnite** *Neohibolites* was recovered from the Hunstanton Formation and the bivalve *Inoceramus crippsi* from the Cenomanian. This is now grassed over.

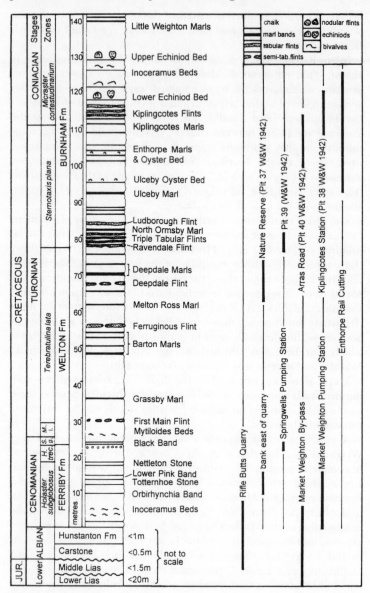

Figure 15.1 Geological succession in the Market Weighton–Kiplingcotes area.

During construction of the Market Weighton pumping station (SE 889419) in 1966–7, a large excavation exposed the lower part of the Cenomanian chalk up to and just above the Totternhoe Stone. The latter yielded large examples of the ammonite *Parapuzosia (Austiniceras) austeni* and the **brachiopods** *Ornatothyris* and *Rectithyris*, with *Inoceramus crippsi* in lower beds. The underlying Hunstanton Formation and Carstone were exposed in the base of the foundations, where the former yielded the brachiopod *Moutonithyris dutempleana* and the belemnite *Neohibolites minimus*. The Carstone contained many large polished pebbles and the matrix was generally coarser than that exposed in the Melton and South Ferriby quarries further south.

Chalk from the numerous small pits and quarries appears to have been used mainly in the construction of local railway embankments, roads and farm tracks. Some of the softer chalks were also used for the liming of agricultural land.

A number of glacial overflow channels incise the surface of thin **tills** and the underlying chalk of the eastern flank of the Yorkshire Wolds. The main channel is the Goodmanham Channel (previously the Market Weighton **Spillway**), cut between Kiplingcotes and Market Weighton and now a dry valley. It was a direct overflow, by which the drainage of an aligned series of channels along the eastern side of the Wolds was taken into the Vale of York (de Boer *et al.*, 1958). The height of flow probably originated at 82 m O.D., with the outlet at about 52 m O.D. Some dry gullies can still be seen, the best known of which runs down to Rifle Butts Quarry (Fig. 15.2, Locality 1). The disused railway track from Beverley to Market Weighton follows the broad, flat base of the spillway. Some parts of the fairly steep-sloping sides of the spillway exhibit grooved horizontal ridges which may have been formed by fast-moving meltwaters cutting through the chalk as the levels of the flow reduced. Extensive deposits of gravels in the Market Weighton area were probably laid down by meltwaters as they flowed into Lake Humber.

Tills (Newer Drift) of Devensian age cover the eastern flanks of the Wolds, but thin away at about 62 m O.D. These clays contain irregular-shaped chalk fragments, Cheviot **igneous** rocks, Silurian greywackes, sand streaks, laminated silts (containing lumps of till) and chalk gravels and flints of **morainic** origin.

EXCURSION DETAILS

Roadside parking is available at Locality 1, Rifle Butts Quarry, and Localities 2 and 3 are within easy walking distance. Proceed by car to locations 4–5, 6–7 and 8 following the route shown on the map (Fig. 15.2). Parking on verges is possible at all locations and a car park is located at the rear of Grannies Attic at Kiplingcotes Station.

Locality 1, Rifle Butts Quarry, a Yorkshire Wildlife Trust Nature Reserve (SE 898426). It is necessary to gain permission to enter from the Warden (Mr G. Scaife, 24 Rossington Road, Hunters Bar, Sheffield S11 8SA; tel: 0742 660663), or the key holder (Mr M. J. Horne, 28 Salisbury Street, Hull HU5 3HA; tel: 0482 46784). The geological section here is managed by Hull Geological Society. It is subject to erosion in the winter months and instability of the overlying chalk. Protective measures designed to prevent further deterioration of this important exposure include the erection of a protective canopy in 1993, kindly funded by English Nature and the Geologists' Association Curry Fund. The site is an **S.S.S.I.** and *hammering is prohibited*.

This is the only known exposure in the region at the present time where the attenuated Jurassic succession and early Cretaceous unconformity resulting from the effects of the Market Weighton Block can be observed. The lowest beds contain large ferruginous nodules in a brown gritty matrix and are thought to be of Middle Lias (early Jurassic) age. These are overlain by thin remnants of Carstone, a ferruginous sandy deposit containing polished pebbles, and about 1 m of nodular red chalk of the Hunstanton Formation (Albian, early Cretaceous). The sequence is capped by fractured and faulted Cenomanian (late Cretaceous) grey and white chalk of the Ferriby Formation. In the past, the Hunstanton Formation has yielded the brachiopods *Moutonithyris dutempleana*, *Platythyris capillata*, the belemnite *Neohibolites minimus* and the **echinoid** *Hemiaster* sp. Fossils from the Cenomanian chalk are the bivalve *Inoceramus crippsi*, and echinoids *Holaster subglobosus* and *Camerogalerus cylindricus*.

Locality 2, bank above and east of Rifle Butts Quarry (SE 901427). Permission for access is required from the landowner (Mr P. R. Sawyer, Rectory Farm, Goodmanham; tel: 0430 72434). Several small, ridged, horizontal exposures in the chalk occur in the side of the valley, possibly due to either soil creep, or furrowing by ice movement or meltwaters. These exposures are mainly confined to the Lower Pink Band occurring above the Totternhoe Stone in the Ferriby Formation (Fig. 15.1), although fragments of the ammonite *Parapuzosia (Austiniceras) austeni* (mainly confined to the Totternhoe Stone at this horizon) have been found on the scree. The Pink Band yields the rare

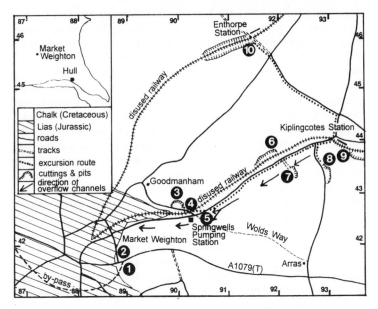

Figure 15.2 Sketch map of the Market Weighton–Kiplingcotes area.

small belemnite *Belemnocamax boweri,* together with brachiopods *Terebratulina etheridgei* and *Concinnithyris concinna,* and the echinoid *Camerogalerus cylindricus.*

Locality 3, Springwells pumping station (SE 900426). Permission for access is required from the landowner (Mr P. R. Sawyer, Rectory Farm, Goodmanham; tel: 0430 72434). A single, narrow-banded exposure, similar to Locality 2, and about 1 m wide, can be seen from the road about 250 m northeast of the pumping station in the south side of the valley. The unit seen is the Black Band, a series of khaki marls with dark-coloured bands in the middle part, also known as the Plenus Marls. This horizon occurs at the top of the *Holaster trecensis* Biozone and just below the top of the Cenomanian Stage, forming an important widespread marker horizon in England, northwest Germany, northern France and in boreholes in the North Sea. Its average thickness in Yorkshire is 0.5 m, and 1 m at Buckton Cliffs on the coast east of Speeton.

Locality 4, Kiplingcotes Pit, a Yorkshire Wildlife Trust Nature Reserve (SE 916435) (Pit 37 of Wright & Wright (1942)). For parties of more than 6 people, it is necessary to seek permission from the Warden (Richard Hewer) or the Trust (10 Toft Green, York YO1 1JT; tel: 0904 659570). The site is an S.S.S.I. and *hammering is prohibited.*

Access is via the reserve. Note the broad, flat valley floor of the Goodmanham Channel. This former rail-side pit exposes horizontal beds of the Welton Formation, fairly high in the *Terebratulina lata* Biozone of the Turonian chalk, and although the lower beds are obscured by scree, it is still possible to examine the Lower and Upper Deepdale Marls near the top of the exposure (Fig. 15.1). Fossils include bivalves of the *Inoceramus lamarcki geinitzi – I.l. cuvieri* group, the brachiopods *Concinnithyris* and *Orbirhynchia*, and the echinoid *Salenia granulosa*, as well as the first appearance of the distinctive echinoid *Infulaster excentricus.*

Locality 5, pit in lane opposite Locality 4 (SE 918434) (Pit 39 of Wright & Wright (1942)). Permission for access is required from the landowner (Mr D. Hiles, Goodmanham Lodge Farm, Goodmanham; tel: 0430 810678). This small exposure, about 5–6 m thick, is thought to occur in the lower beds of the *Sternotaxis plana* Biozone near the base of the Burnham Formation. The four thick tabular flints seen may represent the Ravendale and Triple Tabular Flints, although this cannot be confirmed due to the apparent absence of diagnostic fossils. A shallow trench in the pit floor has recently yielded a few fossils, including fragments of inoceramid bivalves, the brachiopod *Orbirhynchia* and the echinoid *Echinocorys.*

Locality 6, Arras Road Pit, Kiplingcotes (SE 928433) (Pit 40 of Wright & Wright (1942); Whitham (1991)). If working, permission for access is required from T. Woodliffe, Yapham, Pocklington, York YO4 2PH; tel: 0759 302172. The section in this pit, recently worked and greatly extended, exposes about 12 m of the mid part of the Burnham Formation, from just below the Enthorpe Marls, a series of four marl bands in 2.5 m of chalk, up to the lowest unit of the Kiplingcotes Flints. The three Kiplingcotes Marls are well exposed in the higher part of the sequence. Fossils include the echinoids *Sternotaxis placenta, Micraster corbovis,* brachiopods *Pycnodonte vesicularis, Gibbithyris semiglobosa, Orbirhynchia* sp., the **coral** *Parasmilia,* and several species of inoceramid bivalves. The important rare bivalve *Didymotis? uermoesensis* occurs just below the middle Kiplingcotes Marl and marks both the boundary between the *Sternotaxis plana* and *Micraster cortestudinarium*

Biozones and the international boundary between the Turonian and Coniacian Stages. This horizon also marks the upper limit of the range of *S. placenta*.

Locality 7, Kiplingcotes Station Quarry (SE 932437) (Pit 38 of Wright & Wright (1942)). Permission for access is required from Grannies Attic, Station House, Kiplingcotes; tel: 0430 810284. The section in this disused quarry exhibits the three Kiplingcotes Marls spread over about 2 m, with the overlying three semi-tabular Kiplingcotes Flints occupying about 2 m of the succession. Wright & Wright (1942) discovered iron-stained lenticular patches of nodular chalk containing large numbers of gastropods and bivalves preserved in iron oxide, thought to have been saved from destruction or excessive alteration on the sea floor by the collapsed shells of large ammonites. Fossils can still be found on the quarry floor in loose blocks, including the echinoids *Echinocorys scutata*, *Micraster* sp., several species of inoceramid bivalves, and the brachiopod *Orbirhynchia* sp.

Locality 8, Enthorpe railway cutting (SE 906456–914459; (? Pit 45 of Wright & Wright (1942)). Permission for access is required from the landowner (Mr Emmerson, Rossmoor Farm, General Lane, Melbourne, Near York). The disused railway cutting at Enthorpe is about 0.75 km long and trends east–northeast. Access is difficult, as banks are overgrown, and care should be taken. About 30 m of Burnham Formation chalk is exposed, the lowest 16.5 m in the *Sternotaxis plana* Biozone, with the lowest beds marked by the Ulceby Marl at the southwest end of the cutting. The upper 13.5 m is referred to the *Micraster cortestudinarium* Biozone with the highest beds seen near the old station bridge (Whitham 1991). Fossils from the *S. plana* Biozone are similar to those found at Arras Road and the same sequence of beds occurs, including the Enthorpe Marls, and the Kiplingcotes Marls and Flints. The basal beds of the overlying *M. cortestudinarium* Biozone yield numerous specimens of the echinoid *Echinocorys scutata* and less common examples of *Micraster*. Several species of inoceramid bivalves occur, including *Cremnoceramus inconstans*, *C. schloenbachi*, *C. deformis* and *Inoceramus lamarcki*.

16 · The Lower Jurassic rocks between Staithes and Port Mulgrave

Colin Scrutton *University of Durham*

PURPOSE

To examine a gently **dipping** coastal sequence of mid Lias (early Jurassic) rocks, from the Staithes Sandstone Formation through the overlying Cleveland Ironstone Formation and the succeeding Grey Shale, Mulgrave Shale and Alum Shale Members of the Whitby Mudstone Formation. The succession is rich in fossils, principally **ammonites**, **bivalves**, **belemnites** and **trace fossils**. The Cleveland Ironstone Formation, Mulgrave Shale and Alum Shale have all been exploited historically.

LOGISTICS

In Staithes, cars and buses can park in the car park, 300 m on the right from the junction with the A174 (NZ 781184) (Fig. 16.1). It is not advisable, and for coaches not permitted, to drive down the hill closer to Staithes harbour. At Port Mulgrave (NZ 797177), there is limited parking for cars at the top of the cliff. Coaches are prohibited from the short road between the A174 and the coast, but can park in a layby immediately north of the junction on the A174. The distance along the foreshore from Staithes to Port Mulgrave is no more than 2.5 km but may occupy 3–4 hrs, depending on time spent in observations. A cliff-top footpath links Port Mulgrave and Staithes for a return journey on foot. The section is suitable for large parties.

Note: The section is tide dependent. ***The traverse should be started on a falling tide and care taken to leave the foreshore 3 hours before high tide.*** The foreshore may be slippery in parts and involves one scramble over boulders. The cliffs are high and minor falls frequent so *safety helmets should be worn*.
    Staithes is an **S.S.S.I.** so hammering of the outcrop is prohibited.

Maps
O.S. 1:50 000 Sheet 94 Whitby; O.S. 1:63 360 Tourist Map of the North York Moors; B.G.S. 1:63 360 Sheet 34 Guisborough.

GEOLOGICAL BACKGROUND

During the Lower Jurassic, the Staithes area was part of the Cleveland (or Yorkshire) Basin, bounded by land to the north and at times to the west, by the Market Weighton Block to the south, and passing offshore into the **fault**-bounded Sole Pit Trough. Shelf seas covered the area to depths of up to 100–200 m. The Lias Group is a sequence of dominantly mud-grade sediments reaching about 420 m thickness in North Yorkshire (Fig. 16.2). The Staithes Sandstone Formation, of Pliensbachian age, lies at the top of a shallowing and coarsening upwards sequence. Deepening seas above led to a return of fine-grained sediments, but the shales of the Cleveland Ironstone Formation are punctuated by a series of ironstone bands, each formed at the top of a small-scale shallowing upward cycle. Renewed **transgression** close to the Pliensbachian-Toarcian boundary initiated the Whitby Mudstone Formation, including the distinctive, hydrocarbon-rich Mulgrave Shale Member and the widely worked Alum Shale Member. A final shallowing event led to an influx of sandy material forming the Blea Wyke Sandstone Formation capping the Lias, but over most of the region these younger sediments are missing and the Middle Jurassic rests directly on the Alum Shale Member at Port Mulgrave. The cause of sedimentary cyclicity in the Lias is probably a combination of global sea level rise and fall and local earth movements. The best-known evidence for the latter is the **unconformity** of about 25 m amplitude below the Main Seam of the Cleveland Ironstone Formation that causes it to **overstep** lower units to the south down to a level below the Avicula Seam.

Ammonites are variably common more or less throughout the sequence, which is thus well dated. Both trace and body fossils are richly represented at various levels, with bivalves the dominant invertebrates.

Three units in this sequence are of former economic importance. The Cleveland Ironstone Formation was worked in the 19th and 20th centuries, sporadically on the foreshore between Staithes and Port Mulgrave where the seams are thin, but extensively inland in the Cleveland Hills where the Main Seam reaches 3.8 m thick. The last mine closed in 1964. The ore was the original raw material for the local iron and steel industry. Within the background sequence of dark grey shales, the ironstones are scattered, orangey-brown weathering beds composed principally of **siderite** and **chamosite** and variably **oolitic**. Their method of formation has been controversial. Current opinion is that they formed in shallow marine inshore waters, at times of very slow sedimentation. Large amounts of iron, derived from **lateritic** weathering of a landmass in the area of the Pennines, were periodically introduced by river systems transporting ferric oxides and hydroxides as a colloidal suspension, or absorbed on the surface of organic material, or as oxide films on clay minerals. Siderite and chamosite were probably formed under reducing conditions by early **diagenetic** processes, with the iron salts replacing and displacing freshly deposited sediments below the sediment-water interface.

Scattered masses of a tough, shiny, dense black material called jet, occurring in the Mulgrave Shale Member, formed the basis of local manufacture of personal and domestic ornaments, particularly in the second half of the 19th century. Jet was formed from logs of araucarian wood transported into the sea, which became waterlogged and then sank to the reducing sea floor. Diagenetic alteration and compression under these conditions produced this unusual result. The shales of the Mulgrave Formation are rich in hydrocarbons and are an example of an oil source rock. Laboratory distillation yields 54–86 litres per ton of sulphurous oil (Hemingway *in* Rayner & Hemingway, 1974).

The Alum Shale Member was extensively worked for alum, a mordant (fixing agent) in the dyeing industry, from the early 17th to mid-19th century. The shale was burnt for a year or more in huge heaps (up to 30 m diameter and 15 m high) over beds of brushwood. **Pyrite** in the shale was oxidized to form iron and aluminium sulphates, which were extracted by steeping in tanks of water. Potash alum was produced by adding ashes produced by burning seaweed, and later ammonium alum was made by adding urine. On evaporation, the alum crystallized before the impurities (mainly salts of iron), which could then be pumped off. The precise moment at which to stop heating for the maximum yield of alum was determined by floating an egg in the liquor as a hydrometer!

This account is based in part on Hemingway (*in* Hemingway *et al.*, 1968; Rayner & Hemingway, 1974) and Rawson (*in* Rawson & Wright, 1992).

EXCURSION DETAILS

The bus park at Staithes is on the edge of a 60 m marine wave-cut platform. The Boulby headland 3.5 km to the west is pitted by alum,

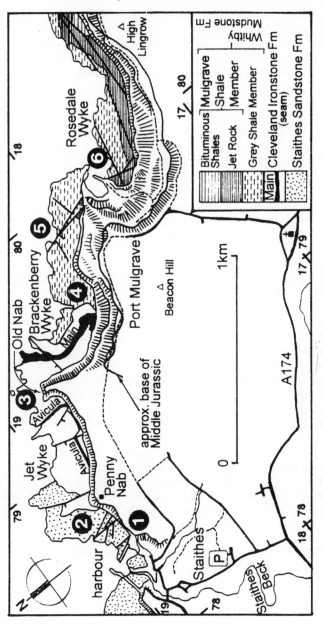

Figure 16.1 Geological map of the foreshore between Staithes and Port Mulgrave (modified from Rawson *in* Rawson & Wright, 1992).

jet and ironstone workings and capped by the massive delta-top sandstones of the Middle Jurassic Saltwick Formation. Immediately inland from it can be seen the headgear of the Boulby potash mine, which extracts potassium salts from a level in the Permian at about 1100 m depth. The road to the harbour descends the deep, post-glacial gorge cut by Staithes Beck in the ferruginous, fine- to medium-grained sandstones and siltstones of the Staithes Formation.

Locality 1 (NZ 784188). Within the harbour, the Staithes Formation is well exposed in the cliff-foot ledges to the east. Note the cyclic development of the beds clearly defined by the sedimentary structures. Each unit has a sharp, erosive base, with shelly channel-floor lag deposits, overlain by sands showing planar and some hummocky **cross-stratification**, with parallel and ripple lamination above. Increasing numbers of trace fossils progressively destroy the depositional fabric towards the finer-grained top of each unit. The sequence reflects the activity of intermittent, shallow-water storm events eroding the tops of previous cycles and depositing each unit under a waning current. The muddy bed tops were colonized by burrowing organisms, including bivalves such as *Protocardia*, during the intervals between major storms. Fossils are common, including *Protocardia truncata*, *Oxytoma inequivalvis*, the **scaphopod** *Dentalium giganteum* and belemnites. Ammonites are not common but evidence for the *Prodactylioceras davoei* and succeeding *Amaltheus margaritatus* **Biozones** has been established within the formation.

Cross the inner end of the east pier of the harbour, now fortified by large blocks of a Scandinavian **gneiss**, onto the foreshore flats. In the cliff, the transition upwards into the shaley Cleveland Ironstone Formation can be seen. One-third of the distance to the headland, faulting is clear in the cliff, displacing the prominent ironstone bands near the top of the face. Bedding plane surfaces on the foreshore exibit excellent interference ripples at one point and many accumulations of fossils. As well as mixed assemblages, almost monospecific shell **coquinas** of *Protocardia* can be found, whilst elsewhere, this shallow-burrowing bivalve can be seen *in situ* in its burrow. Clusters of belemnite guards demonstrate current alignment. Fragments and even substantial trunks of wood may also be found. Clusters of fossils often act as loci for the formation of sideritic **concretions**, giving the rock a dark, reddish-brown colour.

Locality 2 (NZ 788189). At the first headland, Penny Nab, scattered ironstone concretions occur in shales a few metres from the cliff at the

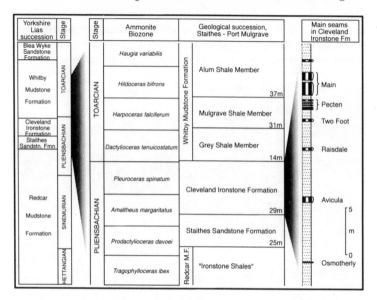

Figure 16.2 Lower Jurassic (Lias Group) succession in Yorkshire, with details for the Staithes–Port Mulgrave area.

base of the Cleveland Ironstone Formation. With the change in **lithology**, there is a reduction in **benthonic** fauna and an increase in **pelagic** fauna, principally belemnites and ammonites. It is possible to find species of the ammonite *Amaltheus* around here. Some of the ironstone concretions contain a rich fauna of bivalves with **brachio-pods** and small ammonites. Immediately beyond the headland, there is an excellent view to the southeast, across the wide wave-cut platform of Jet Wyke. The Cleveland Ironstone Formation is superbly exposed in the cliffs and on the foreshore, with the ironstone bands standing out as thin, more resistant, orangey-brown units. The succession of bands, from the Avicula Seam to the Main Seam, can be readily identified in the cliff section (Figs. 16.2, 16.3).

Cross Jet Wyke towards the next headland of Old Nab. On the traverse, scattered ammonites and belemnites can be found in the shales. The effects of the minor faults which cut the succession can best be seen where they displace the ironstones, whose detailed character can be examined in several places, preferably on the foreshore well away from the base of the cliffs. The Avicula Seam, for example, which is repeated on the foreshore by the faulting, shows an irregular top, with specimens of *Oxytoma cygnipes* (formerly *Avicula*) and other bivalves, burrows formed by *Protocardia*, and a **conglomeratic** base. The rock is a fine-grained sideritic mudstone, containing pale green ooliths of chamosite which are best seen on fresher surfaces.

Figure 16.3 Cleveland Ironstone Formation in Jet Wyke, looking west. The Avicula Seam forms the bedding surface in the foreground; higher seams can be identified in the cliff. *Photo*: C. Scrutton.

Locality 3 (NZ 794188). The ironstones are best seen at Old Nab, where richly fossiliferous surfaces can be examined on the cliff-foot ledges which extend round into Brackenberry Wyke. Among the bivalves *Pseudopecten equivalvis* reaches large size, occurring together with *Oxytoma cygnipes*, *Pleuromya costata*, *Pholadomya* and *Protocardia*, the brachiopod *Tetrarhynchia tetrahedra*, and rare pleuroceratid and amaltheid ammonites. Fossil wood can be found and more rarely vertebrate remains. On Old Nab itself, where the Main Seam has been mined by pillar and stall workings, the trace fossil *Rhizocorallium*, excavated by crustaceans, is widespread on the stall floors, exposed by marine erosion. It consists of horizontal parallel tubes with striated walls, occasionally with the terminal U-bend visible. On the intervening pillars, thin branching tubes of the trace fossil *Chondrites* are common. The shale backfill of an old **adit** can be seen at one point. In Brackenberry Wyke beyond Old Nab, the Main Seam has been extensively quarried and mined, the material having been carried to Port Mulgrave for shipping by a cliff-foot tramway. *The old adits are extremely dangerous.*

Locality 4 (NZ 795182). The base of the Grey Shale Member crosses onto the foreshore about two-thirds of the distance across Bracken-berry Wyke to the next headland. In the lower part, the pale grey-weathering shales contain six rows of reddish-brown-weathering sideritic concretions. Higher calcareous nodules, often found loose on the foreshore here, yield *Dactylioceras tenuicostatum*, belemnite guards and contain crystals of **sphalerite**. Pyrite is common in the shales.

At the southeastern end of Brackenberry Wyke, fallen blocks of medium to coarse-grained deltaic sandstones of the Middle Jurassic Saltwick Formation, which form the top of the cliffs, obscure the cliff face and block the foreshore. Scramble over the blocks with care.

Locality 5 (NZ 798180). Immediately beyond the obstruction, isolated blocks of Saltwick Formation on the foreshore are perched on shale pedestals which the blocks have protected from erosion. These are the Sheep Stones. At the level of the cliff foot, the Grey Shale Member, with common *Dactylioceras* spp., passes up transitionally into the Mulgrave Shale Member. This latter is a sequence of dark to black, laminated pyritic shales rich in hydrocarbons. Freshly broken rock smells strongly of oil. Calcareous concretions, some pyrite-skinned, are common and may contain ammonites such as *Harpoceras falciferum*, with rare specimens having oil in their chambers. Flattened specimens of *Harpoceras*, often pyritized, are abundant in the shales, together with the pelagic bivalves *Pseudomytiloides dubius* and *Bositra radiata*. Note the lack of any benthonic fauna, indicating reducing conditions at the sea floor. Signs of excavations for jet can be seen. Adits, *which are extremely dangerous*, were usually roofed by a thin bed of limestone concretions, the 'Top Jet Dogger'. Rare masses of jet occur in the 3 m of beds below this level. Small faults bring the Grey Shale Member up to cliff-foot level again just before Port Mulgrave.

Locality 6 (NZ 799177). The harbour at Port Mulgrave was built for shipping ironstone, principally from mines 3.5 km to the west. For the last 1.5 km, the tramline entered an inclined tunnel to reach the harbour at shore level; the bricked-up exit can be seen in the cliff at the back of the bay. The piers were severely damaged in the storm surge of 1953. The Alum Shale Member is exposed in the cliffs above Rosedale Wyke just beyond Port Mulgrave. A detour may be made to the southeastern part of Rosedale Wyke where the Top Jet Dogger reaches shore level and beyond which, the upper part of the Mulgrave Shale Member may be examined. The cliff-top can be gained at Port Mulgrave by a steep path immediately behind the harbour.

17 · Lower–Middle Jurassic sequences between Whitby and Saltwick

Martin Whyte and **Mike Romano** *University of Sheffield*

PURPOSE

To study the succession and depositional features of the Lower Jurassic (Whitby Mudstone Formation) to Middle Jurassic (Ellerbeck Formation), the relations between the Lower and Middle Jurassic and the local exploitation of the geology. The sequence is very fossiliferous, with **ammonites**, **belemnites**, fish, **bivalves**, **trace fossils**, dinosaur footprints and plants.

LOGISTICS

A one-day excursion which can be divided into two half-days – Whitby to Saltwick Nab, and Saltwick Bay (Fig. 17.1). The most convenient of several car parks within Whitby is the Abbey Plain pay-and-display (NZ 902113) (Fig. 17.1). Descend either Church Lane or Church Steps; at the bottom go straight ahead and take one of the small closes leading from Tate Hill to the shore. On the shore turn right and proceed to the landward end of the East Pier (Locality 1). Access to the shore can also be gained down a close off Henrietta Street (turn right at the bottom of the Church Steps). However, due to subsidence, the Spa Bridge at the far end of Henrietta Street is closed and cannot at present (May 1993) be used as a means of access to the shore.

To return from Saltwick Bay, ascend to the well-marked cliff-top path. The total walking distance is about 6 km.

Note: The potential dangers of this part of the coast cannot be over-exaggerated. The foreshore between Whitby and Saltwick Nab is normally only accessible for about two hours on either side of low tide. Some combinations of tide and meteorological conditions may prevent any access to the shore, or may considerably shorten the available access time. **Tide tables must be consulted** (times of high water are normally posted daily on the west end of the bridge in Whitby) *and this part of the excursion must be carried out on a falling tide*. The rising tide crosses the flat rocks of The Scaur (Fig. 17.1) very rapidly and it is essential that Saltwick Nab is rounded before the passage along the west side of the Nab (NZ 914113) is blocked by the tide.

Within Saltwick Bay, access on and off the shore is possible at most states of the tide, though the lowest parts of the succession are only visible at very low tides. On a rising tide, care should be taken to avoid being cut off on slight elevations on the flat expanse of Saltwick Scar.

Fine debris is continually falling from the cliff faces and there are intermittent larger falls; thus working at or close to the base of the cliff should be avoided and *hard hats must be worn*.

Maps

O.S. 1:50 000 Sheet 94 Whitby; O.S. 1:63 360 Tourist Map of the North York Moors; B.G.S. 1:63 360 Sheet 35 & 44 Whitby and Scalby.

GEOLOGICAL BACKGROUND

At the start of the late Lower Jurassic, a **eustatic** change in sea level led to increased water depths within the Yorkshire Basin and initiated a prolonged phase of mud deposition. These mudrocks, the Whitby Mudstone Formation, are subdivided into a number of distinct units or members. Succeeding the basal Grey Shale Member (Excursion 16; not seen here), the Mulgrave Shale Member was deposited in anoxic bottom waters and consists of bituminous shales, which since they were not disturbed by any bottom fauna are finely laminated. The overlying Alum Shale Member formed in less oxygen-poor conditions in which the presence of a limited bottom fauna disturbed the laminae. At Ravenscar the Alum Shales can be seen to pass up into siltstones and sandstones, but in the Whitby area these and the uppermost beds of the Alum Shale Member have been removed in a regional phase of uplift, gentle folding and erosion which took place at the end of the Lower Jurassic.

Middle Jurassic deposition started with the shallow marine Dogger Formation. The overlying Ravenscar Group is predominantly non-marine in character but is subdivided by a number of marine horizons. Only the lowest part of the Ravenscar Group – namely the Saltwick and Ellerbeck Formations – can be seen at Whitby. The Saltwick Formation is a fluviatile sequence of shales, siltstones and sandstones while the Ellerbeck Formation is a unit of marine **clastics**.

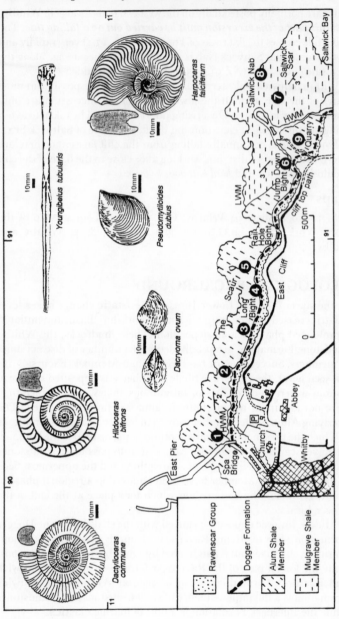

Figure 17.1 Simplified geological map of the Whitby to Saltwick Nab area.

EXCURSION DETAILS

Locality 1 (NZ 902115). From the low concrete wall below the Spa Bridge a good view can be had of the western end of East Cliff. The lower third of the cliff is made up of shales of the Alum Shale Member (Lower Jurassic). Resting on these is a 0.75 m ironstone (the Dogger Formation), overlain by the sandstones, shales and siltstones of the Saltwick Formation (30 m). Above these are orange-weathering marine sandstones of the Ellerbeck Formation (6 m).

Between Localities 1 and 2, strong jointing in the Alum Shale has been exploited by marine erosion to produce small embayments and caves in the cliff. These joints **strike** parallel to the north–south Whitby **Fault**, which passes through the harbour region. Notice also the low-angle westerly-**dipping joints** which could easily be mistaken for bedding but which cut across bands of **concretions**.

Locality 2 (NZ 904115). Do not pass beyond this point, the last of the joint controlled headlands, unless you are confident of being able to reach Saltwick Nab, or of returning to this point, before the tide turns and rises to the base of the cliff.

As the tide retreats wide expanses of the Alum Shale Member are exposed on the shore in front of Localities 1 to 5. This shale contains abundant specimens, preserved either crushed or in the round, of the deposit-feeding bivalve *Dacryomya* (formerly *Nuculana*) *ovum* (Fig. 17.1). Most are articulated and some are in life position. In addition the shale contains large fossilized driftwood logs, belemnites, the bivalve *Gresslya* and the ammonites *Dactylioceras* and *Hildoceras* (Fig. 17.1). The latter genus, named after the Abbess of Whitby, St Hilda (614–680), recalls the local legend, recorded by Scott in *Marmion*, that the fossil ammonites were snakes which St Hilda had turned to stone. The arms of Whitby include three snakestones in which a snake's head has been carved onto the ammonite. Except where preserved within concretions, only the elongate body chambers of the ammonites, which may extend for more than a whole whorl, are preserved uncrushed. The driftwood is often partly **pyritized** and pyritized burrow systems may also be found. Horizons of concretions, variously made of **siderite**, **calcite** and pyrite, have allowed a detailed stratigraphy of the shale to be established (Howarth, 1962) and show that between Localities 1 and 4 the shale is on the western limb of a shallow, southwards-plunging **syncline** (Fig. 17.1).

Locality 3 (NZ 906114). To the west of a prominent rockfall the Dogger, which has descended gradually towards shore level with an easterly dip, thins and is almost completely cut out by a sandstone-filled channel in the Saltwick Formation. The western margin of the channel complex is clearly marked and within the channel large coalified logs are common at the base. The eastern margin is obscure though there are siltstones and fine sandstones modified by considerable synsedimentary disturbance. In fallen blocks a variety of material from higher in the cliff can be examined and good examples of ripple marks and U-shaped burrows can be seen. In the cliff large vertical U-shaped burrows extend down from the base of the Dogger into the Alum Shale and within the latter there are large calcareous concretions with **cone-in-cone** structure.

Locality 4 (NZ 908113). The synclinal axis passes through and controls the centre of Long Bight and between here and the next headland (Locality 5), the Dogger Formation rises in an inclined bench close to the foot of the cliff. The Dogger is a coarse, sometimes pebbly, ferruginous sandstone containing berthierine (**chamosite**) **ooids**. Larger clasts within the Dogger include reworked phosphate nodules and fragments of ammonites and belemnites which have been derived from the upper part of the lower Jurassic and demonstrate the discordance between the Alum Shale Member and the Dogger Formation. At the junction between the two units large burrow systems can again be seen to pipe material from the Dogger down into the shale. The fine sandstones and siltstones above the Dogger contain an abundance of plant remains (Whitby Plant Bed) and examples of a variety of foliage types may be found on fallen blocks on the shelf of the Dogger. In places large sandstone-filled root systems extend down from the Saltwick Formation into the Dogger and even into the Alum Shale.

Locality 5 (NZ 909114). At the headland there is a large rockfall, and some blocks with a 0.05 m skin of reddish sideritic siltstone adhering to their base may be found. This is the Unio Bed, so called since it contains occasional specimens of the fresh-water bivalve *Unio*, which lies 6.2 m above the Dogger. Between Locality 5 and Rail Hole Bight (NZ 910112) examination of the fallen blocks on the upper shore will reveal several which contain dinosaur footprints. *Do not damage these blocks.* The blocks come from at least two horizons within the Saltwick Formation: the Unio Bed, and a sandstone about 6 m higher in the sequence. Several types of bipedal tridactyl prints (Fig. 17.2) can be

Figure 17.2 Tridactyl dinosaur footprint, Saltwick Formation, Rail Hole Bight. The lens cap is 50 mm diameter. *Photo*: M. Romano.

found and parts of the track of a sauropod have also recently been recognised (Whyte and Romano, 1993). Raking tridactyl prints appear to have been made by dinosaurs which were swimming. On the flat of The Scaur, away from the cliff, shales of the Alum Shale Member with their typical fauna are still exposed, but are now on the eastern limb of the syncline, and can be followed in descending sequence.

Locality 6 (NZ 913112). At the base of the cliff between Jump Down Bight and Saltwick Nab (Fig. 17.1) a double row of pyritic carbonate nodules and sideritic lenses marks the boundary between the Alum Shale Member and the Mulgrave Shale Member. This marker band is known as the Ovatum Band as it contains very occasional specimens of *Ovaticeras ovatum* and other ammonites. Thin (0.15 m) sideritic mudstone bands can be seen 6.3 m above and 5.6 m below the Ovatum Band.

Continue round, or through the gaps in, Saltwick Nab into Saltwick Bay.

Locality 7 (NZ 916112). On the flat expanses of Saltwick Scar the well-laminated bituminous shales of the Mulgrave Shale Member can be examined. The shales contain flattened and pyritized specimens of the ammonite *Harpoceras* and the **epiplanktonic** bivalve *Pseudomytiloides* (Fig. 17.1). The belemnite *Youngibelus* also occurs in normal, bullet-like and epirostrate forms. The epirostrum is a hollow cylindrical extension of the guard and has invariably been crushed during preservation (Fig. 17.1). Dark phosphatic fish fragments may also be found.

Locality 8 (NZ 915115 to NZ 919112). On the outer edge of the shore, large discoidal carbonate concretions (up to 5 m in diameter and 0.3 m thick), known as the Millstones, make a prominent upstanding feature. These preserve within them the sedimentary lamination and rest in a thinly laminated limestone (0.2 m). Beds below this can only be conveniently examined at very low waters, when just under 2 m of very bituminous shale with pyrite-skinned calcareous concretions may be seen. In the past these beds, which lie within the lower part of the Mulgrave Shale Member, were a source of jet but this is now seldom found *in situ*.

Locality 9 (NZ 914112). The vast amphitheatre at the back of Saltwick Bay has been created by working of the alum shale. Note the red, burnt shale which has been dumped on the top of the landward parts of Saltwick Nab. The path to the cliff-top leads through the old quarry and in its back wall (NZ 913111) ascends over beds of the Saltwick Formation. The Unio Bed makes a small waterfall to the east of the path. At the cliff-top turn right and take the path leading back to the Abbey Plain car park. En route there are good views of the cliff and shore below. In the cliff note the channelling which can be seen in the upper part of the Saltwick Formation.

18 · Lower and Middle Jurassic rocks between Robin Hood's Bay and Hawsker Bottoms

John Senior *University of Durham*

PURPOSE

To view one of the finest Lower Jurassic sections in Northern Europe, starting with the Redcar Mudstone Formation (Calcareous Shales; Lower Lias) in the Robin Hood's Bay dome structure and ending with the Alum Shales Member (Whitby Mudstone Formation; Upper Lias). The overlying Dogger and Saltwick Formations (Aalenian, Middle Jurassic) are exposed in cliff sections at Hawsker Bottoms.

LOGISTICS

This is quite a strenuous day, entirely dependent on favourable tides. Park in the Old Station car park in Robin Hood's Bay (NZ 950055). There are toilets, pubs and cafes in Bay Town, but none en route.

Note: The beach traverse takes at least 4 hours to complete at a moderate pace for a fit person and with few stops. Start on a falling tide (2–3 hours below low tide). ***Do not attempt this section at the wrong state of tide with an on-shore wind as there are many places (marked on the sketch map) where the tide rushes in and you could be cut off***. There is only one way up the cliff at the end of the section at Hawsker Bottoms. At a few points you may gain sanctuary and wait for the tide to recede (take a box of matches to light a drift-wood fire for warmth or to attract attention).

Wear a safety helmet. Try to keep clear of the cliffs as there is a constant rain of debris (from shale fragments to sandstone blocks of many tonnes weight). Try to go in pairs so that one can watch the cliff while the other looks at the geology; indeed this is a lonely section so *inform someone* (i.e. Coastal Wardens) where you are going and at what time you intend returning to Robin Hood's Bay.

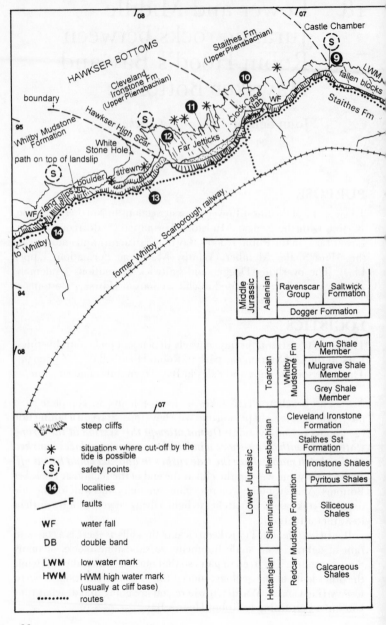

		steep cliffs
	*	situations where cut-off by the tide is possible
	(S)	safety points
	14	localities
	—F	faults
	WF	water fall
	DB	double band
	LWM	low water mark
	HWM	HWM high water mark (usually at cliff base)
	••••••••	routes

Middle Jurassic	Aalenian	Ravenscar Group	Saltwick Formation
		Dogger Formation	
Lower Jurassic	Toarcian	Whitby Mudstone Fm	Alum Shale Member
			Mulgrave Shale Member
			Grey Shale Member
	Pliensbachian		Cleveland Ironstone Formation
			Staithes Sst Formation
		Redcar Mudstone Formation	Ironstone Shales
			Pyritous Shales
	Sinemurian		Siliceous Shales
	Hettangian		Calcareous Shales

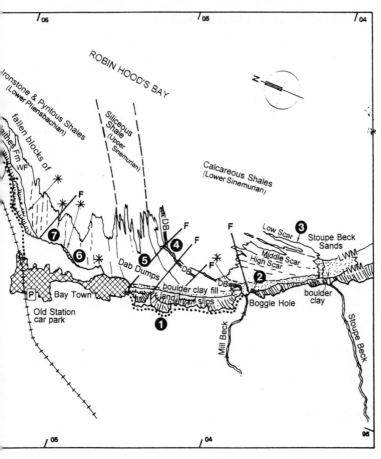

Figure 18.1 Map of the foreshore between Robin Hood's Bay and Hawsker Bottoms, with the geological succession for the area.

At the end of the section when you have ascended the very steep cliff path at Hawsker Bottoms, there is a brisk cliff-top walk of at least 1 hour's duration back to Robin Hood's Bay.

Maps

O.S. 1:50 000 Sheet 94 Whitby; O.S. 1:63 360 Tourist Map North York Moors; B.G.S. 1:63 360 Sheets 35 & 44 Whitby & Scalby.

167

GEOLOGICAL BACKGROUND

This 11.5 km section is on the northern limb of the Robin Hood's Bay dome structure, one of several inversion structures (intra-Jurassic) found in the Cleveland–Sole Pit Trough Depositional Basin (Kent *in* Rayner & Hemingway, 1974). This well-defined and classically exposed equidimensional structure (Fig. 18.1) is truncated to the east by the north-south Peak **Fault**, considered to be both a late Liassic synsedimentary fault and a sinistral transcurrent fault which has displaced the seaward part of the dome possibly some 8 km southwards (Hemingway *in* Rayner & Hemingway, 1974). The base of the Lias (Hettangian Stage) is not exposed even at the lowest tides in Robin Hood's Bay and there may be some slight discrepancy in the actual thicknesses of the lower Liassic sequences which are exposed on the extensive wave-cut platform. A summary geological succession is given in Fig. 18.1.

There are thick deposits of **tills** in the central areas of Robin Hood's Bay and it has been suggested that these Late Quaternary deposits infill valley features at two points: The Sands, just South of Bay Town (NZ 954045), and at Stoupe Beck (NZ 958035). Indeed the base of the pre-glacial valley at Stoupe Beck seems to be below present sea level. These tills contain **erratics** from a variety of sources and supply exotic beach pebbles in the central section of the Bay (identifying them provides an interesting pastime when waiting for the tide to go out!). The cliffs predominantly composed of till are unstable and subject to extensive landslips but occasionally the tills can be seen to be divided by a central sandy sequence.

EXCURSION DETAILS

From the Old Station car park (NZ 950055), pause at the top of the hill to appreciate the panoramic views of the bay and the dome structure visible at low tide, then descend the hill through Bay Town to the Landing slipway. At this point it would be an advantage to take the coastal cliff path southwards to Boggle Hole.

Locality 1 (NZ 952046). There are fine views from the path of the minor faults exposed on the beach (at Locality 4) which radiate from the centre of the bay and the dome structure.

Locality 2 (NZ 956041). At the exit of Mill Beck onto the beach at Boggle Hole identify the 'Double Band' which forms a prominent scar feature to the south of the beck at the base of the cliff. This Double

Band forms a prominent marker horizon within the *oxynotum* **Biozone** (Sinemurian).

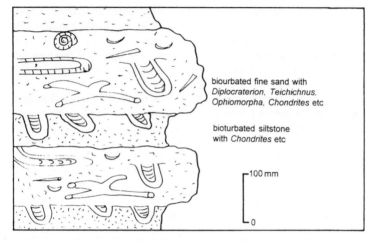

biourbated fine sand with *Diplocraterion, Teichichnus, Ophiomorpha, Chondrites* etc

bioturbated siltstone with *Chondrites* etc

100 mm

0

Figure 18.2 The 'Double Band' at Boggle Hole. These two prominent bioturbated fine sandstones containing a variety of trace fossils form a useful marker horizon on the foreshore.

Locality 3 (NZ 959038). Walk out into the centre of the bay to the limit of the tide and then work back up-sequence over the harder continuous scars (beach features of calcareous siltstones, fine sandstones and nodule horizons) with intervening softer siltstones and shales (also with nodules) which constitute the Calcareous Shales (lower Redcar Mudstone Formation) at this locality. At the furthest extremity you will be within the *obtusum* Biozone (although the reefs furthest out to sea to the southeast contain the **ammonite** *Arnioceras* indicating the *semicostatum* Biozone). About halfway between High Scar and the Double Band at the base of the cliff the ammonite faunas change to *Gagaticeras, Oxynoticeras* and *Epararietites* indicative of the *oxynotum* Biozone. All the sediments exposed as scar features or interleaving shales/siltstones are fossiliferous, with body fossils such as **bivalves** (*Gryphaea, Pleuromya*), **crinoids** (*Pentacrinites*) and numerous **belemnites**. These sediments are also extremely **bioturbated** with widespread *Chondrites* together with more substantial **trace fossils** such as *Teichichnus, Rhizocorallium, Ophiomorpha* and *Diplocraterion* usually associated with the more indurate levels.

At some levels within the softer shales and siltstones large, isolated, flat, subcircular, iron-rich, **concretions** can be seen. These are usually highly bioturbated and sometimes contain *Pentacrinites*, belemnites and ammonites. These have been interpreted as 'scours', where bottom currents winnowed out the finer material leaving marginally coarser-grained sediments and shell debris behind, which then attracted iron **diagenesis**. These 'scours' form a sporadic but integral part of the entire section to be viewed for the rest of the day up to the top of the Cleveland Ironstone Formation.

Return to the Double Band at the base of the cliff at Boggle Hole and follow this prominent beach feature across Mill Beck (where it is displaced slightly at a small northeast–southwest fault).

Locality 4, Dab Dumps (NZ 956047). Around the foreshore between Boggle Hole and Bay Town (known as Dab Dumps) there are a series of small faults associated with the dome structure of Robin Hood's Bay. The throw on these faults can be illustrated using the Double Band as the datum horizon on the foreshore.

Locality 5 (NZ 955048). The sediments above the Double Band contain the ammonite *Echioceras* indicative of the *raricostatum* Biozone. These form the upper parts of the Siliceous Shales.

Opposite the slipway at Bay Town, rare ammonites in the shales of Ground Wyke Hole indicate the start of the Ironstone/Pyritous Shales (Lower Pliensbachian). All ten subzones of the Lower Pliensbachian have been determined in the Ironstone/Pyritous Shales on the north side of Robin Hood's Bay between Bay Town and Castle Chamber. Ammonites are sporadic and poorly preserved in these sediments (which are characteristically cyclic shale-silt units with prominent ironstone concretion levels) but the genera *Acanthopleuroceras*, *Apoderoceras*, *Platypleuroceras*, *Tropidoceras* and *Androgynoceras* are represented. Most of the beds also contain a variety of bivalves, belemnites, **brachiopods** and wood debris; they are also very bioturbated, commonly with *Chondrites*, but also with *Rhizocorallium*, *Ophiomorpha* and *Teichichnus*.

Locality 6 (NZ 953052). From this point (where curious vertical 'starlike' **pyrite** bodies may be seen in the shales) onwards, the sediments of the *ibex* Biozone are rich in the large bivalve *Pinna*. Over beds some 26.5 m thick the communities of *Pinna* can be seen either in life position, with the open aperture probably facing the predominant bottom current direction (the planed-off bivalve shells having a distinctive lozenge appearance), or with the large triangular shells current sorted and lying parallel to the bedding planes (storm redistribution?).

Locality 7 (NZ 954054). Throughout the remaining part of this section almost to Castle Chamber, horizons of red **sideritic** nodules are well displayed in cliffs and on the foreshore where they often display a ramifying and connected appearance. These ironstone nodules usually have **septarian** centres. A prominent nodule horizon may be seen at the base of the cliff with diffused reddish margins and cream-coloured septarian interiors. This is near a prominent normal fault (you might like to pause and try to work out the throw on this fault).

Working northeast towards Ness Point (North Cheek) the slight northern dip on the northern limb of the Robin Hood's Bay dome brings in younger horizons. There are rare ammonites in this part of the section (in nodules and as pyritic nuclei in shales/siltstones), bivalves are common (i.e. *Pseudopecten, Pleuromya* and other myids and *Gryphaea*) and there are at least three thin and impersistent limestone horizons comprised of current sorted *Gryphaea* shells (mixed with belemnites and other bivalves). Cliff exposures near Dungeon Hole (NZ 953054) show these Pliensbachian sediments to have numerous fining upwards cycles often with minor erosion gutters.

Locality 8 (NZ 960061). Just past the waterfall and shipwreck remains at Ness Point and just in view of Castle Chamber, look for a particular ironstone nodule bed on the foreshore. This 0.10 m thick composite bed of sideritic nodules has large subvertical burrows in the top, filled with **chamositic oolitic** ironstone (the first oolitic ironstone in the Yorkshire Jurassic Basin). Some 9 m above this oolitic horizon is one of several curious ironstone horizons; this one is bimodal in origin with small concretions (0.10 m in diameter) at the top of a 0.20 m concretionary bed.

From Ness Point on to Castle Chamber large fallen blocks of sandstone from the Staithes Formation may be seen on the foreshore. The stratigraphical top of these blocks often have rippled surfaces and are covered with well-preserved shell debris, including *Pseudopecten, Protocardia, Gryphaea, Liostrea* and the **scaphopod** *Dentalium*, the latter often displaying well-developed current orientation. At Bulmer Steel at the base of the cliff and on the foreshore look for a 3.5 m section of grey siltstones with grey nodule horizons where *Oistoceras figulinum* might be found (indicating the top Subzone of the *davoei* Biozone).

Locality 9, Castle Chamber (NZ 960067). The Ironstone Shales (shales/siltstones) at the top of the Redcar Mudstone Formation grade imperceptibly into the shallow-water siltstones/sandstones of the Staithes Formation. Some 4.5 m below the floor of Castle Chamber is a prominent laminated sandstone, the first real arenaceous horizon of the Staithes Formation. The small sandstone cliff overhang at Castle Chamber provides a good shelter/safety point and the section there forms the biostratigraphical boundary between the Lower and Upper Pliensbachian, with the first *Amaltheus* some 0.3 m below the roof sandstones. The **cross-laminated** sandstone/siltstone horizons which form the floor and roof of Castle Chamber (usually with oyster beds at the base of both) are exposed on the foreshore between Castle Chamber Point and the Cow and Calf Rocks. Both sandstone units exhibit scour gutters at the base.

Walking northwest towards Clock Case Nab, you will pass over shallow water sediments, particularly sandstones with nests of *Protocardia truncata* (often the centres for sideritic diagenesis). Occasional finds of *Amaltheus stokesi* in these sediments indicate the base of the *margaritatus* Biozone.

Locality 10, Clock Case Nab (NZ 956071). A thin split ironstone nodule horizon can be seen at the base of Clock Case Nab. Looking northwest across the embayment called Far Jetticks towards Hawsker High Cliff and High Scar, there is a fine view of the upper Middle Lias (*spinatum* Biozone) on the foreshore section with a thick sequence of the Upper Lias (Whitby Mudstone Formation: Grey Shale Member to Alum Shale Member) in the cliff section above.

Locality 11, Far Jetticks (NZ 953073). The Upper Middle Lias section at Far Jetticks, some 12.5 m thick, may be compared with that seen in the Staithes–Port Mulgrave section (Excursion 16). All the subzone index ammonites may be found on this section together with many belemnites, bivalves and nests of *Tetrarhynchia*.

While in the vicinity of Hawsker High Cliff look (*with extreme caution*) at the fallen material at the base of the cliff. Pyrite-skinned nodules contain *Harpoceras exaratum* and *H. falciferum* (index fossils of the Mulgrave Shale Member), while grey nodules containing *Dactylioceras* and *Hildoceras* indicate the Grey Shale and Alum Shale Members.

Locality 12, Hawsker High Scar (NZ 951077). The calcareous sandstone that forms the top of the scar, which may involve a 3 m scramble, is some 3.20 m below the top of the Middle Lias. The sediments here indicate an important event boundary within the Yorkshire Basin, where the shallow-water sediments of the Cleveland Ironstone Formation abruptly change to deeper-water sediments of the Whitby Mudstone Formation (Grey Shale Member).

Locality 13, White Stone Hole (NX 950076). The Grey Shale Member is reasonably well exposed here near the base of the subcliff. The Mulgrave Shale Member is well exposed 200 m to the northwest, where the continuous concretion horizon of the Top Jet Dogger and the Whale Stone concretions some 2 m below can be seen at the base of the subcliff (the productive jet horizon on the Yorkshire coast is between these two concretion bands).

At this point the beach section becomes less clear as it is littered with deltaic sandstone blocks from the cliff above. From White Horse (NZ 949078) onwards the foreshore section is largely obscured by large landslips. At the top of this landslip complex is a path of sorts (it continually changes owing to movement) which should be followed to Pursglove Stye (NZ 945082). Here the steep path (often slippery and subject to landslip) up the heather-covered slope of Alum Shales should be taken to the top of the cliff at Locality 14 (NZ 946081) where you will meet the coastal path.

Locality 14 (NZ 946081). Before finally getting to the top of the cliffs at Hawsker Bottoms, an interesting minor detour involves walking southeast for 0.1 km at the base of the vertical Middle Jurassic sandstone cliff. The sections in the Saltwick Formation are particularly good with excellent channel features, but at the end of this path is also an excellent exposure of the ferruginous sandstones of the Dogger Formation (Aalenian, Middle Jurassic). This marine sandstone contains sporadic bivalves and often has a remainié bed at the base consisting of phosphatic pebbles and ammonite fragments eroded from the Upper Lias beneath. There is a stratigraphical hiatus at the junction of the Lias with the Dogger.

On reaching the cliff-top footpath, walk back to Robin Hood's Bay and the car park, stopping to look at the Alum Shale workings at the top of Clock Case Nab (NZ 954070).

19 · The Middle–Upper Jurassic sequence between Cayton Bay and Yons Nab

Martin Whyte and **Mike Romano** *University of Sheffield*

PURPOSE

To study the succession, depositional history, and palaeontology (including plant beds) of the Middle Jurassic (Lebberston Member) to Upper Jurassic (Lower Calcareous Grit Formation), the Red Cliff **Fault**, Quaternary **tills** and examples of mass movement.

LOGISTICS

This is a full-day excursion best commenced on a falling tide so that Locality 6 will be reached at low water. If tide times dictate, the excursion may be carried out in the reverse direction. Walking distance is about 5 km.

Take the small track which leaves the A165 in the hollow (TA 068840) about 200 m south of the traffic lights at the junction between the A165 and the minor road to Cayton. This leads into Killerby Park where cars may be parked for a small fee. Coaches may also be parked here by prior arrangement with Mr D. R. Hindley, Killerby Park, Killerby Cliff, Cayton Bay, Scarborough, North Yorkshire, YO11 3NR (tel: 0723 582495).

Note: At high tides water may reach the base of the cliff, especially on the east side of Yons Nab. *Care must also be taken at Locality 6* where the rising tide quickly fills gullies on the landward side of the Millepore Bed in front of Yons Nab. *Safety helmets must be worn close to the cliff base.*

Maps

O.S. 1:50 000 sheet 101 Scarborough & Bridlington; B.G.S. 1:63 360 Sheet 54 Scarborough.

GEOLOGICAL BACKGROUND

The Middle Jurassic of the Yorkshire basin consists largely of fluviatile and deltaic sandstones with marine intercalations (Ravenscar Group). This excursion examines the upward **facies** transition from one of these marine intercalations (Millepore Bed of the Lebberston Member) through a mixed marine and non-marine sequence (Yons Nab Beds of the Lebberston Member) into non-marine deposits (Gristhorpe Member). This can be contrasted with the more abrupt junctions of the Gristhorpe Member with the overlying marine Scarborough Formation, and of the Scarborough Formation with the deltaic Scalby Formation. The latter contact may represent a depositional break of several million years. The Scalby Formation is the highest subdivision of the Ravenscar Group and in late Middle Jurassic (Callovian) times fully marine conditions were established by a **transgression** from which a sequence of limestones (Cornbrash Formation), clays (Cayton Clay Formation) and sandstones (Osgodby Formation) were deposited, the latter interrupted by minor phases of **tectonic** tilting and erosion. In the Upper Jurassic (Oxfordian) deepening marine conditions gave rise to the deposition of widespread silty clays (Oxford Clay Formation), which pass gradually up in a shallowing sequence into the Lower Calcareous Grit Formation. Despite its name the latter is a fine-grained sandstone. It has a **calcite** cement and is very rich in **sponge** spicules.

The considerable thickness of rocks which can be examined here is in part due to movement on the Red Cliff Fault. This fault probably has a long history of movement and in the Mesozoic was one of a suite of faults which formed the eastern margin of the Peak Trough (Milsom & Rawson, 1989).

EXCURSION DETAILS

From the car park take the path that leads directly down a gully to the shore (Fig. 19.1). Once on the shore, turn right (east). Killerby Cliff is entirely made of till which has been much affected by mass movement. Several World War II pill boxes can be seen in various stages of descent from the cliff-top. The till fills a pre-glacial valley, which was cut to below present-day sea level, and eastwards the slope of the valley side can be seen in section with rockhead gradually rising from shore level up to the cliff-top. The character of the cliff thus changes and becomes more precipitous, to give the striking face of High Red Cliff. This cliff is composed of three units: the lower vertical part is

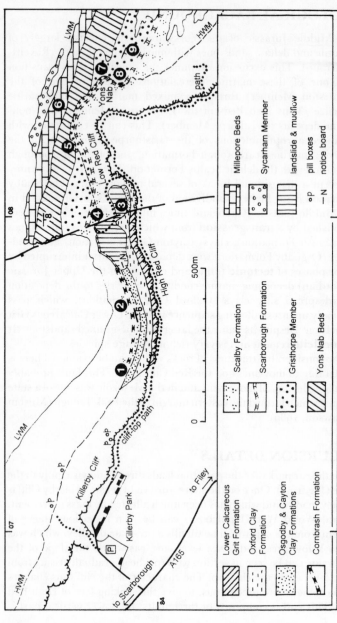

Figure 19.1 Simplified geological map of the Cayton Bay to Yons Nab area.

made of sandy Osgodby Formation (13 m), the upper vertical portions are made of the Lower Calcareous Grit Formation (25 m) and these are separated by the steeply sloping face of the softer Oxford Clay Formation (40 m). In the Oxford Clay minor rhythmic alternations of harder and softer bands, visible here, may represent the effects of small climatic changes related to periodic variations in the Earth's orbit (Milankovitch cycles). It is interesting that rhythms on a similar scale continue into the Lower Calcareous Grit despite the major change in lithology.

Locality 1 (TA 075841). The Osgodby Formation can be examined by climbing up at the western end of its main outcrop. At the top the Hackness Rock Member (2 m) consists of sandy berthierinitic (**chamositic**) **oolite** and limy sandstone containing **belemnites**, *Gryphaea* and occasional **ammonites**. The underlying Redcliff Rock Member (11 m) contains ferruginous sandstones, bands of sandy berthierinitic oolite and is more silty towards its base. Some horizons contain an abundance of **bivalves** and sparse ammonites. The boundary between the Hackness Rock and Redcliff Members is difficult to locate precisely, though the intervening Langdale Member is missing here due to erosion (Wright 1968). The underlying Cayton Clay (3 m), Cornbrash Limestone (0.4 m) and Scalby Formations are usually covered by beach sand. However the Cornbrash Limestone Formation can be seen at Locality 2, where it forms a low ledge within the boulders on the upper beach and about 20 m out from the base of the cliff. Between Locality 1 and Locality 2, note the large, differenti-ally weathering, spheroidal **concretions** (up to 2 m in diameter) developed in the lower part of the Redcliff Rock Member. Fallen blocks of Osgodby, Oxford Clay and Lower Calcareous Grit Forma-tions can also be examined but attest to the considerable dangers of working in this area. The silty clays of the Oxford Clay contain poorly preserved ammonites, while the well-cemented sandstones of the Lower Calcareous Grit show an abundance of branching, network-like, burrow systems (*Thalassinoides*).

Locality 2 (TA 077841). The Cornbrash Limestone Formation is an impure, nodular limestone containing ribbed oysters (*Lopha*) and occasional specimens of other bivalves (including *Trigonia*, *Pholadomya* and *Entolium*). At its base, U-shaped burrows (*Rhizocorallium*), pre-served in **siderite**, extend down into greyish silty sandstones which here represent the top (1 m+) of the Scalby Formation. Shales of the Cayton Clay Formation may occasionally be seen beneath boulders between the Cornbrash outcrop and the cliff base. In the cliff the sandstones of the Redcliff Member show oblique, westerly-dipping planes, and fallen blocks contain a fauna of bivalves (including *Pinna*, *Trigonia*, *Gervillia* and *Entolium*) and belemnites.

From Locality 2 it is best to continue above the zone of slippery green seaweed to where a prominent notice board (Fig. 19.1) advises that it is not possible to walk to Filey at shore level. Here the cliff runs inland behind a large, degraded, landslip. Either scramble round the margin of the slip at shore level or climb onto the slip and follow the path which runs close to its outer edge. At the far end the path crosses an active mud flow, where the footing can be very soft and muddy as it descends again to the beach at Locality 4 (TA 080842).

Here, Low Red Cliff is clearly different in geological character from High Red Cliff as a result of displacements on the Red Cliff Fault. The fault can be traced on the shore from the truncation of beds on its eastern side and the fault plane outcrops on the upper shore. The trace is obscured under the mud flow but the fault reappears in the cliff at the rear of the flow (Locality 3).

Locality 3 (TA 081841). Ascend to the west of the mud flow. Evidence of recent movement of the mud flow can usually be detected in longitudinally grooved mud surfaces and transverse crevasse-like gashes. The Red Cliff Fault is a westerly **downthrowing** normal fault which almost completely cuts out the Oxford Clay. The apparent vertical displacement is thus about 35 m. Small subsidiary faults can be seen on either side. Coarse crystalline calcite occurs in patches along fault planes and in joints within the Oxford Clay Formation, and fragments may be found in the scree at the cliff-foot. Return to Locality 4.

Locality 4 (TA 080842). The western end of Low Red Cliff is made up of lenticular white sandstones and grey siltstones at the base of the Scalby Formation. In places there is abundant, fine or coarse, coalified plant debris. Some of the plant material is also **pyritized** and weathering of this has covered the cliff face with a bright yellow sulphurous bloom. The geometry of the channel sandstones is variable, and **cross-bedding**, soft sediment deformation and mud-flakes can also be seen. About 30 m to the east the underlying Scarborough Formation, a thin development (2.8 m) of limy shales with two brown ironstone bands close to the top (Fig. 19.2), can be found at the base of the cliff. Towards the centre of the formation, an abundance of crushed shells, with ribbed oysters (*Lopha*) and other

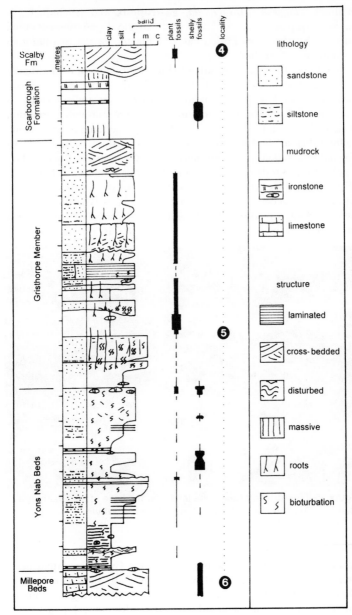

Figure 19.2 Sedimentological log of the section between Yons Nab and the Red Cliff Fault.

molluscs (*Trigonia*, *Meleagrinella*, **gastropods** and belemnites), is obvious. In places the basal beds of the Scalby Formation cut down into the Scarborough Formation and the top of the Scarborough Formation is disturbed.

From here to the next headland (Locality 5) one moves gradually down succession within the Gristhorpe Member but exposures are variable depending on the amount of beach cover and till slippages from the cliff-top. Immediately under the Scarborough Formation there is a 1.4 m thick sandstone with fine cross-bedding (some authors include this, as the Helweth Beck Member, within the Scarborough Formation). Other prominent horizons in downward sequence (Fig. 19.2) are a sandstone containing vertical rootlets of horsetails (*Equisetum*), a **bioturbated** carbonaceous sandstone lens (Fig. 19.3) and a carbonaceous siltstone with plant remains (Gristhorpe Plant Bed). The latter rests on a highly bioturbated sandstone with vertical roots which is the basal bed of the Gristhorpe Member (Fig. 19.2).

Figure 19.3 Bioturbated sandstone lens near the base of the Gristhorpe Member. The hammer is 350 mm long. *Photo*: M. Whyte.

Locality 5 (TA 083843). The basal bed of the Gristhorpe Member is well seen where the top bed of the Yons Nab Beds (Lebberston Member) also forms a prominent ledge. On the ferruginous upper surface of this bed can be found internal moulds of bivalve shells and valves, including *Pholadomya*, *Trigonia* and *Pteroperna*. Some of the bivalves are in life position. There are also some large vertical U-shaped burrows. The sequence of the Yons Nab Beds (Fig. 19.2) is displayed down the shore between Locality 5 and the prominent ledge of the Millepore Bed (Lebberston Member) (Locality 6). In the upper parts there are alternations of sandstone and shale, and poorly preserved bivalves may be found at several levels. The lower parts of the sequence are, apart from a thin ripple-marked and burrowed sandstone, entirely shale with occasional ironstone bands and concretions. Apart from small burrows the shales are only fossiliferous immediately above the Millepore Bed.

Locality 6 (TA 084843). The top of the Millepore Bed is well seen on the foreshore and is a sandy oolitic and **bioclastic** limestone (2 m) with well-developed cross-bedding. Fragments of the **bryozoan**, *Haploecia straminea*, from which the bed derived its name, can be found but are not common at this locality. The lower parts of the Millepore Bed are cross-bedded calcareous sandstones (7 m) which can, at low water, be seen to rest on sandstones of the Sycarham Member.

From Locality 6 look back at the cliff at a **strike** section of the Gristhorpe Member between Locality 5 and the next headland, Yons Nab (Locality 7). Small channels and other lateral changes can be detected within this sequence. Return to the cliff base close to Locality 5 and walk east along the ledge formed by the top bed of the Yons Nab Beds. Approaching Yons Nab, notice how the bed is removed by a northeast–southwest trending channel which cuts down from the Gristhorpe Member into the Yons Nab Beds.

Locality 7, Yons Nab (TA 085842). The complex channel-fill sandstones are well displayed on the shore in front of Yons Nab. To the east the upper beds of the Yons Nab Beds reappear on the eastern side of the channel. Immediately in front of Yons Nab, the siltstones of the Gristhorpe Plant Bed rest on the channel sandstones and are overlain by a bioturbated carbonaceous sandstone. However these beds are often concealed by beach gravels which here usually contain an abundance of pyrite nodules and fragments, some of which show traces of woody structure. At the base of the cliff on the east side of Yons Nab a sandstone with ironstone concretions and plant fragments contains occasional poorly preserved specimens of the fresh-water bivalve *Unio*.

Locality 8 (TA 085841). From Locality 7 to Locality 8, the cliff shows an ascending sequence through the Gristhorpe Member and the Scarborough Formation, which can be compared with the sequence between Localities 4 and 5 (Fig. 19.2). The cross-bedded sandstone below the Scarborough Formation is well exposed here, as are the fossiliferous beds of the Scarborough Formation.

Locality 9 (TA 085840). Here a large channel within the Scalby Formation cuts down into the top of the Scarborough Formation.

About 200 m south-southeast of Locality 8 (TA 086838), climb up the clay slopes to a path that leads to the cliff-top (the lower parts of the path have been destroyed by mass movement). Take the cliff-top path over High Red Cliff back to Killerby Park. This route provides excellent views both of the coast and of the Vale of Pickering. Both Gristhorpe Cliff to the east and the headland of Scarborough Castle to the north show the same middle to upper Jurassic sequence as at High Red Cliff. Alternatively return along the shore to the path down from Killerby Park.

20 · Jurassic, Cretaceous and Quaternary rocks of Filey Bay and Speeton

John Neale *past President, Yorkshire Geological Society* and **John Catt** *Rothamsted Experimental Station, Harpenden*

PURPOSE

To examine the Devensian glacial deposits, interglacial shell bed, Upper Jurassic Kimmeridge Clay, Lower Cretaceous Speeton Clay and Upper Cretaceous Red and White Chalks exposed in the coastal cliffs of the southeast part of Filey Bay.

LOGISTICS

Parking for a coach or up to 10 cars is available near the cliff-top at Reighton Sands (TA 141763). The coast section is suitable for a large group, and involves an easy walk of about 4 km (plus 4 km return), taking at least 3 hours.

Note: The section is *accessible only for 3–4 hours on either side of low tide. Hard hats should be worn.* Do not stand close to vertical clay sections during and after rain when they are unstable, and do not attempt to walk across soft active mudflows. On the sloping cliffs it is safest to walk only on vegetated areas. The high chalk cliffs beyond are dangerous because of block falls and *should not be approached closely at any time*. The nature of the Red and White Chalk may be studied in foreshore exposures and fallen blocks away from the cliff base.

Maps

O.S. 1:50 000 Sheet 101 Scarborough & Bridlington; B.G.S. 1:50 000 Sheet 55/65 Flamborough & Bridlington.

GEOLOGICAL BACKGROUND

In this section the solid rocks have a low, general southerly, **dip** so that progressively younger rocks occur southward. Marine Jurassic and

183

Lower Cretaceous clays and shales are overlain by the Red and White **Chalk**. A non-sequence occurs at the top of the Jurassic rocks (Kimmeridgian Stage, c. 146–151 **Ma**) and the Portland and Purbeck rocks of the south of England are not developed. The succeeding 10 cm Coprolite Bed is overlain by the Cretaceous Speeton Clay (about 100 m), forming the finest marine Lower Cretaceous section in Britain and equivalent to five of six Lower Cretaceous Stages (c. 136–106 Ma). The Ewaldi Marl, Gault Clay and lower Red Chalk above represent the sixth Lower Cretaceous Stage and the remainder of the Red Chalk and overlying White Chalk form a very full sequence of Upper Cretaceous rocks. The latter is best examined further south in the Flamborough area (Excursion 21).

During the Late Devensian Stage of the Quaternary, ice advanced southwards in the western part of the North Sea area and deposited **tills** blocking the seaward end of the Vale of Pickering. From radiocarbon **dating** of organic remains found above and below the equivalent glacial deposits in Holderness, the ice invaded eastern Yorkshire about 18 000 years ago and finally melted by about 13 000 years ago. Two main tills were deposited – a lower greyish-brown and an upper reddish-brown till. In Holderness these are known as the Skipsea and Withernsea Tills respectively; there they contain more

Figure 20.1 Speeton Shell Bed, between Speeton Clay and Skipsey Till, New Closes Cliff. The spade rests against the basal chalk-flint gravel of the Shell Bed. *Photo*: J. Catt.

chalk than the equivalent tills in Filey Bay, because the ice crossed the main Chalk outcrop between the two areas. The two tills were probably deposited by a single two-tiered ice-sheet. The Skipsea Till originated from ice which moved across southeast Scotland, Northumberland and Durham, whereas the Withernsea Till was deposited by ice which came from the Lake District and crossed the Pennines via the Vale of Eden, the Stainmore Gap and Lower Teesdale. The Lake District/Teesdale glacier was superimposed on the Scottish/Northumberland ice off Teesmouth, and both then moved southwards as a two-tiered glacier.

In interglacial periods before the Late Devensian glaciation the eastern end of the Vale of Pickering was an estuary. Sediment which accumulated in the estuary during an interglacial dated by the amino acid method to approximately 200 000 years ago forms the Speeton Shell Bed, which occurs between the Speeton Clay and glacial deposits on New Closes Cliff.

EXCURSION DETAILS

The lane from the A165 at Reighton village to Reighton Sands traverses several **drumlins** with long axes orientated north-northwest–south-southeast, a local direction of ice movement parallel to the Chalk escarpment. From Reighton Sands car park follow the sloping track to the shore and turn right (southeastwards). The cliffs cut in Pleistocene and Mesozoic clays for the next 2 km are continually changing because of landslipping and coast erosion, so it is impossible to give exact locations of good exposures. Usually about 90% of the cliffs are occupied by landslips, many of which are rotational slips. *In situ* exposures have vertical faces and approximately horizontal planes between till and gravel units.

About 500 m east-southeast of Reighton Gill solid rocks appear in the cliffs from beneath the tills. However sand may be stripped from the beach to provide foreshore exposures of the solid rocks from the Gill onwards. They are divided into Beds A–F, F being the lowest; Beds B–E constitute the Speeton Clay. Minor **folding** in the argillaceous rocks results from the weight of the Chalk above or the pressure of Quaternary ice.

Locality 1. The cliff section from below the car park to the seaward end of the ravine called Reighton Gill (TA 142763 to TA 144762) exposes the Late Devensian tills. Approximately half the cliff is formed of the greyish-brown Skipsea Till, often obscured by downslipped masses of

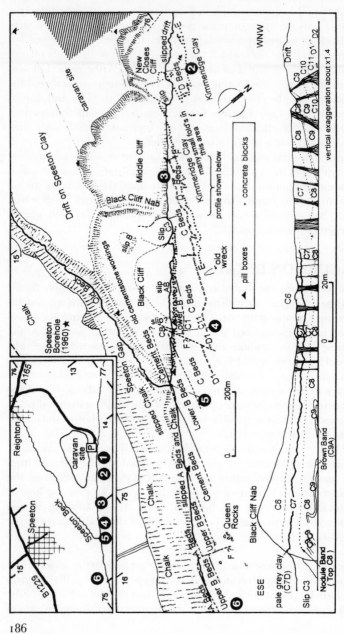

Figure 20.2 Map of the Speeton Clay section (after Neale *in* Rayner & Hemingway, 1974). Inset map shows approach to the coastal section from Reighton.

the overlying reddish-brown Withernsea Till. Thin gravels are often seen between the two tills or in the lower part of the Withernsea Till. At Reighton Gill the junction between the two tills rapidly descends to about a quarter of the cliff height, and within the Withernsea Till on the southeast side of the Gill there is a 2–3 m thick gravel, which rises rapidly in the cliff section for about 100 m southeastwards. Near its southeastern extremity, there is a large contorted raft of grey Jurassic (Kimmeridge, Oxford or Liassic) clay high in the cliff in the Withernsea Till.

Southeast of Reighton Gill, the glacially disturbed surface of Mesozoic clays rises at approximately 88 m/km from below sea level to approximately 30 m O.D. on New Closes Cliff (TA 148759). In places the surface is overlain by a thin chalky gravel sometimes containing estuarine shells, the lateral equivalent of part of the Speeton Shell Bed (Locality 2). The overlying tills are usually less well exposed on the sloping, densely vegetated cliffs than they are on either side of Reighton Gill, but a few metres of weathered Withernsea Till is usually visible at the top of the cliff.

Stone orientation measurements show that Skipsea Till ice flowed northeast–southwest in the Reighton area, whereas the parent ice of the Withernsea Till moved north-northwest–south-southeast, parallel to the long axes of the drumlins, which must be composed mainly of Withernsea Till. The lower part of the tiered ice-sheet preserved the regional ice movement direction, but the upper part was controlled by the local topography, notably the direction of the Chalk escarpment.

Locality 2, New Closes Cliff (TA 146760), some 500 m southeast of Reighton Gill. Approximately halfway up the cliff (TA 14757585) the Speeton Shell Bed is usually exposed between an eroded and contorted surface of Speeton Clay and the Late Devensian Skipsea Till (Fig. 20.1). It consists of 2–5 m of sandy loam, grey below but weathered brown in upper layers, lying between two beds of chalk-flint gravels. Shells within the sandy loam include the **bivalves** *Macoma balthica, Scrobicularia piperata, Cardium edule* and *Mytilus edulis*, and **gastropods** *Littorina littorea, L. rudis, Hydrobia ulvae* and *Utriculus obtusus*, an assemblage indicating temperate estuarine conditions; many of the same species are in fact common in the modern Humber estuary. A microfauna also indicates deposition in shallow brackish water. The chalky gravels above and below the Shell Bed probably accumulated by **gelifluction** in cold periods, so the whole sequence represents a cold–warm–cold oscillation.

The shelly loam often contains narrow shrinkage cracks, probably formed during brief periods of exposure at low water during deposition of the Shell Bed. The loam and chalky gravel above and below are also contorted and faulted. Edwards (in Ellis, 1987) identified two episodes of disturbance: a strong earlier episode of north–south compression which affected the sandy loam, lower chalk gravel and underlying Speeton Clay, and a later weaker northeast–southwest compression which contorted the upper chalk gravel and refolded some of the earlier folds. The later force corresponds with the direction of movement of the lower part of the Late Devensian glacier, which deposited the Skipsea Till. The earlier force raised the eroded top of the Speeton Clay to approximately 28 m higher than its predicted regional level at Reighton, the folds in this clay indicating an outcrop compression of approximately 2:1. The earlier force also pushed the Shell Bed to its present position on New Closes Cliff from a much lower original level of deposition.

The earlier (north–south) force probably resulted from the only other known glaciation of East Yorkshire, which deposited the Basement Till of Holderness, during the Wolstonian Stage (130000–186000 years ago) or earlier. A thin layer of Basement Till also occurs locally above the Speeton Shell Bed on New Closes Cliff, but this is probably a large erratic raft picked up by the late Devensian glacier and deposited in the lowest part of the Skipsea Till. Provisional amino acid dating of *Macoma balthica* shells from the Speeton Shell Bed suggests deposition in the Ilfordian Interglacial (186000–245000 years ago), which implies that the glaciation resulting in initial disturbance of the Speeton Shell Bed and in deposition of the Basement Till was the Wolstonian.

The Upper Jurassic Kimmeridge Clay (F Bed) is exposed in New Closes Cliff, where it appears from beneath the till, and is also seen from time to time in beach exposures (Fig. 20.2). The maximum thickness is 225 m but only the uppermost part is seen in this section. It consists of black **pyritic** shales and paper shales with large **dolomite** concretions. White flattened **ammonites** (*Pectinitites pectinatus*) are abundant, as are small **molluscs** similarly preserved.

The basal Cretaceous E Bed, the **Coprolite** Bed (0.1 m), seen in the area of New Closes Cliff, looks hard and cindery and represents the slowly accumulating sweepings of the old sea floor. It consists of rolled and fragmentary phosphatic and pyritic bivalves, ammonites and bones. In the last century some 500 tons of coprolites (phosphate content 57–61%) were mined annually until 1869 when a landslip closed the workings. The old wooden **adit** props may still be seen occasionally emerging from the eroded base of the cliff.

The D Beds (14.21 m, Berriasian, Valanginian and Hauterivian (part) Stages) are well seen in New Closes Cliff, and consist of black, blue and brown clays which may be **glauconitic**, pyritic or **selenitic**. In this, and subsequent beds up to the Red Chalk, brown phosphatic nodules of various shapes and sizes are common and provide evidence of the very slow accumulation of these deposits on the old sea floor. The D Beds are characterized by ammonites and the robust square-sectioned **belemnite** *Acroteuthis*. Bivalves, **brachiopods** and crustacea also occur and large plesiosaur bones have been found in the higher D Beds. Four thin yellow beds indicate ancient volcanic ashes. The top bed is the Compound Nodular Bed (0.30 m), a series of isolated fossiliferous nodules showing two generations of nodule development indicative of very slow formation.

Locality 3, Middle Cliff (TA 148757). The C Beds (39.02 m, Hauterivian Stage) consist of light and dark grey clays characterized by the torpedo-shaped belemnite *Hibolites jaculoides*. Ammonites occur throughout with *Lyticoceras* (= *Endemoceras*) and uncoiled forms such as *Aegocrioceras* commonest in the lower part and *Simbirskites* in the upper part. These indicate the Hauterivian Stage, although there is still some uncertainty about the exact position of the boundary with the overlying Barremian Stage. A wide variety of other fossils occurs. Some of the phosphatic nodules contain the 'Speeton Shrimp' *Meyeria ornata*.

At the eastern end of Middle Cliff an old landslip brings in the higher beds and forms a belt of disturbed ground stretching for about 350 m between there and Black Cliff (TA 153755). The clays are largely B Beds but examples of the Red Chalk and White Chalk may also be examined. This is convenient if one does not wish to proceed beyond Speeton Beck (TA 155754) to see them *in situ*.

Locality 4, Black Cliff (TA 152755). The B Beds are characterized by the pointed cylindrical belemnite *Oxyteuthis* and three divisions are recognized.

The Lower B Beds (20.94 m, Barremian Stage) crop out in Black Cliff and are dark, blue-grey clays with some intercalations of paler clays. Various forms of pyrite are common and glauconite occurs at some horizons. Besides *Oxyteuthis*, shelly fossils include bivalves, gastropods, large fragmentary ammonites and a rare **echinoid**.

Locality 5, Speeton Beck (TA 155754). The beck forms the southern boundary of Black Cliff and provides a stable and easily recognized marker point in this section. It provides access to Speeton Village or the cliff-top path and is an alternative route to a shore-level return to Reighton Gap at the end of the excursion.

The Middle B Beds or Cementstone Beds (9.75 m, Barremian Stage) occur in the upper part of Black Cliff north of Speeton Beck but at beach level south of it. South of the beck the sections are poor, the clays being much obscured by slippage and fallen debris from the high White Chalk cliffs. The black pyritic clays contain seven bands of large impure limestone nodules of which the lowest three are the most persistent. These nodules have approximately the right proportions of clay and limestone for calcining and grinding to make cement and have hence been called 'Cementstones'. In the last century they were worked in open workings above Black Cliff and also by adits driven into the cliff. They made a light-coloured Roman cement which set rapidly and did not crack on drying. Over 1000 tons a year were sent annually to Hull by coaster and later by railway.

The Upper B Beds (9.14 m, Barremian and Aptian Stages) are very pyritic clays with some browner beds. Poorly exposed, most are Barremian but the highest part has yielded Aptian ammonites.

The Ewaldi Marl (A Beds, 2.79 m, Albian Stage) consists of dark brown streaky clays with green glauconite patches, phosphatic nodules and a basal nodule bed. The typical belemnite is the small torpedo-shaped *Neohibolites ewaldi*.

The Gault Clay (5.99 m, Albian Stage) consists of red-brown clays with some green-grey clays and a thin (0.2 m) band of glauconite with phosphate nodules ('The Greensand Streak') at the base. The small (2–3 cm long) belemnite *'Neohibolites minimus'* indicates an Albian age which is confirmed by rare ammonite finds.

Locality 6, Buckton Cliffs (TA 163751). About 600 m east-southeast of Speeton Beck the Red and White Chalk form the impressive Buckton and Bempton cliffs stretching on to Flamborough Head (Excursion 21).

The Red Chalk (up to 30 m, Albian and Cenomanian Stages) is essentially white chalk coloured by ferric oxide, probably derived from Triassic rocks and incorporated in the limy ooze of the sea floor at the time of deposition. As little as 1% of ferric oxide will give a good red colour. The same belemnite occurs as in the previous beds as well as other fossils, notably terebratulid brachiopods. Ammonites show that the lower 16.10 m of the Red Chalk belong to the Upper Albian. The remainder is placed in the Cenomanian, the lowest stage of the Upper Cretaceous.

The hard limestone of the White Chalk (about 400 m in the Flamborough area, Upper Cretaceous) forms the high cliffs of Buckton and Bempton and is well seen to the south of Speeton Beck. ***Beware of falling debris and the possibility of being cut off by the rising tide.*** The hardness of the chalk in Yorkshire, compared with that of the south of England, is a result of its **calcite** cement. The lowest 44 m are the so-called 'Flintless Chalk'. Above that the development of **flint** in the form of nodules and bands of silica reaches a maximum in the 169 m of the 'Flinty Chalk', to be followed by an upper group of 'Flintless Chalk' about 107 m thick. These thicknesses are only approximate and vary somewhat from place to place. The white chalk contains a wide variety of fossils throughout but they are scattered, often fragmentary and difficult to extract. Large bivalves of the genus *Inoceramus* and sponges are the best known.

21 · The Chalk of Flamborough Head

Richard Myerscough *Past President, Hull Geological Society*

PURPOSE

To examine the most northerly outcrop of late Cretaceous **chalk** in England at Flamborough Head, together with features of the Devensian glaciation, including the buried cliff at Sewerby. The headland has **S.S.S.I.** status for its coastal-scenery, geology and wildlife, being one of the most important coastal nesting sites in Europe.

LOGISTICS

Access to the coast is easy; all the bays have adequate parking (Fig. 21.1). Public transport is limited, but in summer a regular 'Headlander' Little Bus from Bridlington calls at all the localities, which are also linked by a well-maintained coastal footpath.

Note: *All locations must be visited on falling tides*. Times are available from H.M. Coastguard or the Heritage Coast Project. *Safety helmets are recommended* as cliffs are subject to falls and mud slides. Suitable footwear is required as the foreshore rocks can be very slippery.

Maps

O.S. 1:25 000 Sheet TA 26/27 Flamborough; O.S. 1:50 000 Sheet 101 Scarborough & Bridlington; B.G.S. 1:63 360 Sheet 65 Bridlington.

GEOLOGICAL BACKGROUND

The chalk succession exposed between Sewerby and Bempton Cliffs, about 400 m thick, is subdivided on **biostratigraphical** and **lithostratigraphical** criteria (Fig. 21.2). These criteria also distinguish the chalk of Flamborough Head from that of Southern Britain as Northern Province Chalk. The chalk represents slow deposition of

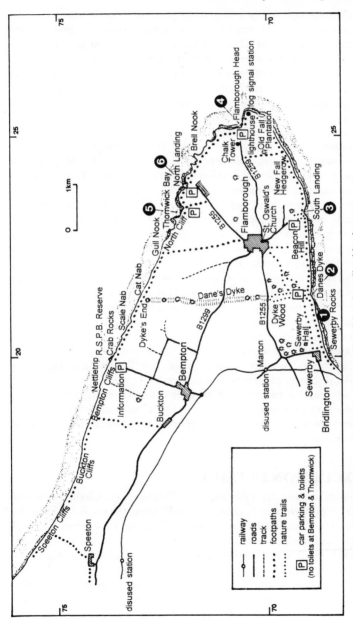

Figure 21.1 Map of the Flamborough area indicating localities described in the text.

193

carbonate material in a clear tropical ocean. **Clastic** material is at a minimum except for **marl** bands, which may represent air-borne ash falls associated with volcanic activity as the proto-Atlantic opened to the south. Within the middle chalk, **flint** is found as nodules and thicker beds, some of which can be used with the marl bands as marker horizons throughout Flamborough and the Yorkshire Wolds. In the upper chalk, large nodules of **marcasite** can be found, often converted to rusty masses of iron carbonate.

In late Cretaceous times, the chalk sea **transgressed** over the **fault**-controlled topography of the Market Weighton Block, and represents a contrast in depositional history to that displayed at Speeton. The earliest beds (Hunstanton Formation or Red Chalk) rest with marked **unconformity** on early Jurassic rocks in the Market Weighton area, with isolated patches of basal **conglomerates** and sands (see Excursion 15). The sea finally covered the block and deepened in the faulted basins to the north and south, with the chalk sections of the Wolds thinner than that on the coast. In the Tertiary, pressure from the east gently **folded** the chalk into a saucer-like basin, producing scarps in the west and north Wolds and reactivating the older marginal faults along the Howardian–Flamborough Fault System, resulting in a compressional/extensional fracture zone running east–west across the Wolds and exposed on the coast. The chalk was compressed and recrystallized to form the resistant Flamborough headland. Marine erosion has exploited the many minor faults associated with the crush belt, forming the magnificent coastal scenery of arches, stacks, caves and coves.

The chalk is covered by **drift** from the most recent Devensian ice-sheet that banked up against the headland to form the Flamborough **Moraine**, which contains exotic **erratics** from Northern England and Scandinavia.

EXCURSION DETAILS

Locality 1, Sewerby (TA 202687): Flamborough Chalk Formation (Sewerby Member), *Inoceramus lingua* **Biozone** (60 m). Reach Sewerby on a minor road off the B1255 from Bridlington. Park at Sewerby Park (Zoo and small Museum, with cafe and toilets), walk to the cliff edge and descend to the beach by the concrete Sewerby Steps, noting the rotational slipping of the Skipsea **Till** along a spring line. The beach is built of chalk boulders, many bored by modern **bivalves**, together with erratics and large blocks of calcrete, a post-glacial gravel cemented by calcium carbonate. The chalk is soft and flintless, with

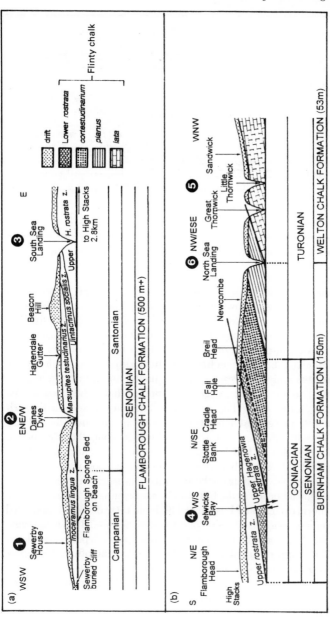

Figure 21.2 Cliff profiles: (a) Bridlington to South Landing; (b) Flamborough Head to Thornwick Bay (based on Neale *in* Rayner & Hemingway, 1974).

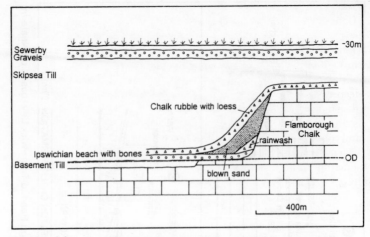

Figure 21.3 Profile of Sewerby buried cliff (based on Myerscough *in* Lewis, 1991).

thin marly partings. Investigation is often prevented by rainwash from above, bringing down mudflows of drift, and by rock falls. In the past, the wave-cut platforms offered good collecting, especially from the Flamborough **Sponge** Bed that stretches from here almost to Danes Dyke, but it is better to collect from beach boulders. Fossils found include bivalves, **echinoids, brachiopods**, starfish plates, **ammonites** and well-preserved hexactinellid and lithistid sponges.

Some 250 m south, the gently dipping chalk cliffs end at the Sewerby Buried Cliff (Fig. 21.3) which displays a section through glacial and interglacial deposits banked against and over the old cliff face. This feature can be traced southwards along the edge of the Yorkshire Wolds to Hessle and into Lincolnshire, and represents an interglacial cliff line of between 116 000 and 128 000 years ago. The exposure varies depending on the amount of slippage, but when it is clear the interglacial beach at the base can be seen resting on a planed wave-cut platform of chalk and Basement Till. From these deposits fragmented mammalian bones have been collected indicating an Ipswichian age. The interglacial beach is covered by rain wash, scree deposits and blown sands, and capped with Skipsea Till, followed by **glaciofluvial** Sewerby Gravels containing mammoth teeth and human artifacts.

Return to Sewerby Steps and the car park or coastal path, or continue east along the beach to Danes Dyke, with many fossils, including sponges, to be found en route.

Locality 2, Danes Dyke (TA 231692): Flamborough Chalk Formation (Danes Dyke Member), *Marsupites testudinarius* (26 m) and *Uintacrinus socialis* (29 m) Biozones. There is a car park on the site of Danes Dyke House (with toilets and a small refreshment shop in summer). Walk through the woods to the beach noting the Iron Age earthwork which cuts across Flamborough Head to isolate its eastern end. The dyke is a deep ravine, now occupied by a small seasonal stream cutting into glacial deposits that filled a much larger glacial **spillway**. The ravine is cut along the Danes Dyke Fault that can be seen as highly fractured and contorted chalk in the cliff section to the west of the drainage pipe. Glacial deposits rest on the planed surface of the chalk. The fault can sometimes be traced across the beach in winter after severe storms have swept the beach clear of sand.

Walking west, the southerly dip brings down the upper part of the *Marsupites testudinarius* Biozone for about 200 m to a prominent group of four boulders on the beach. The thinly bedded, flintless marly chalk is full of the isolated calyx plates (see **crinoid**) of the index fossil, and their density increases upwards through the zone, with complete examples of the stemless calyxes not uncommon, especially along marl bands. Other fossils include echinoids, **belemnites**, brachiopods, and starfish ossicles from faecal pellets.

From Danes Dyke return to the car park or the coastal path, or else, *but only on a falling tide*, cross the Danes Dyke fault, which throws down to the south, and follow the shoreline eastwards out of the bay for 500 m to Hartendale Gutter (TA 221692). For about 200 m the more massive-bedded chalk, with bedding plane **stylolites** formed by loading and solution, is cut in the *Marsupites testudinarius* Biozone, but on approaching Hartendale Gutter, the calyx plates become fewer and the succession passes into the *Uintacrinus socialis* Biozone. This stemless crinoid is present locally and may have been (like *Marsupites*) a deeper-water species swept into the Northern Province, as these two fossils are common at this horizon throughout England. The section at Hartendale Gutter is one of the few British localities for complete specimens, but more commonly they are found as isolated calyx plates or groups of plates and arm ossicles, indicating individuals falling into quiet conditions on the sea floor. Other fossils found include echinoids, brachiopods, **corals**, belemnites and sponges.

Return to Danes Dyke, or continue east to South Landing via the coastal path or beach (only on a falling tide.)

Locality 3, South Landing (TA 231693): Flamborough Chalk Formation (South Landing Member), *Hagenowia rostrata* Biozone (23 m).

197

Take Landings Road from Flamborough to the Heritage Coast Centre (where there is a small display of local geology, toilets and picnic areas). Descend to the beach along the road used for launching boats. The ravine is very similar to Danes Dyke and is probably formed along a fault line. The bay is cut in massive-bedded flintless chalk. The index fossil is very rare and the small echinoid *Hagenowia blackmorei* is found instead. Other fossils include echinoids, belemnites and sponges.

It is not recommended to continue further east on the beach towards Flamborough. The coastal path should be taken to Selwicks Bay.

Locality 4, Selwicks Bay (TA 255708): Flamborough and Burnham Chalk Formations, *Hagenowia rostrata* Biozone. Take the B1259 from Flamborough to the car park by the lighthouse (with cafe, gift shop and toilets), noting the older lighthouse on the golf course. Chalk does not make a good building stone and this is one of the few Flamborough buildings made of it. Walk to the top of the steps to view the bay. The vertical chalk cliffs contrast with the grass-covered slopes of the glacial drift, which support a great variety of animal and plant life, especially orchids. Walk down to the top of the new steps. At low tide the geology of the bay is well displayed, as are marine erosion features, especially the prominent stack (known locally as Adam).

Descend to the beach (best at low water). The chalk is cut by the Selwicks Bay Fault, downthrowing about 20 m to the north, and part of the Howardian–Flamborough Fault Zone that runs east–west across the Wolds and marks the reactivated edge of the Market Weighton Block. The main fault zone is marked by a large mass of **fault breccia**, cemented by crystalline **calcite**. The complex nature of the bay is best revealed on the wave-cut platform by walking north across the bay starting at the prominent brown flint band that marks the junction of the flintless Flamborough and flinty Burnham Formations. The fault breccia is a complex structure of fractured blocks with several stages of tension and compression indicated by cross-cutting calcite **veins.** On the north side of the bay the Flamborough Chalk Formation is steeply dipping away from the fault towards the small stream, where the beds are truncated by another, low-angle fault which can easily be traced across the wave-cut platform. On the south side of the bay, the Burnham Chalk Formation reappears in a cove known as Monk Hole. All around the bay, small faults and joints, with both horizontal and vertical **slickensiding** and calcite veins, criss-cross the chalk cliffs and beach, resulting from reactivated movement along the deep-seated faults. Within the chalk, compressional features can be seen, notably above the warning sign at the entrance to Monk Hole. Marine erosion has eroded along the weaker fault lines in the otherwise hard chalk to create a wide range of coastal features such as caves, coves, arches and stacks. *These should only be explored on a falling tide.* Fossils are uncommon in the hard crystalline chalk but include echinoids and belemnites.

The beach has many erratics, including semi-precious **agates** and **cornelians**. A purple sand often accumulates in patches and is largely composed of **garnet**.

Return to the car park or walk north along the cliff to Thornwick and North Landing. All cliff walks display magnificent coastal features, with a wide variety of nesting birds in spring and summer.

Locality 5, Thornwick Bay (TA 234722): Burnham and Welton Chalk Formations, *Stenotaxis planus* (38 m) and *Terebratulina lata* (60 m) Biozones. Take the B1255 from Flamborough to the Viking Hotel and then follow a rough road to the cafe. Descend the cliff path into Great Thornwick Bay which displays massive-bedded flinty chalk. The flint and marl bands form easily traced marker horizons around the bay and into Little Thornwick, for example the Feruginous Flint (easily recognized by its reddish colour), and the Ravendale Flint 1 m below, marking the junction of the Welton and Burnham Chalk Formations, and the zonal boundary. Erosion features, excavated along faults and joints, are seen in both bays. Fossils are scarce in the hard recrystallized chalk but include echinoids, brachiopods and bivalves.

Locality 6, North Landing (TA 238720): Burnham and Welton Chalk Formations, *Sternotaxis planus* and *Terebratulina lata* Biozones. Take the B1255 from Flamborough to the car park at North Landing (with cafe and toilets). Walk down to the beach via the slipway to the Lifeboat Station. North Landing is a very narrow bay and is probably fault controlled, with the back of the bay choked with till. In summer, boats frequently go out from here to view the birds and pass by the highly contorted chalk at Old Dor and Scale Nab (TA 205736). The chalk is massive and flinty, with a marl band forming a prominent ledge dipping into the bay and into the fault line cave on the north side. A band above it contains oysters, brachiopods and the index fossil, *Sternotaxis planus*. The flints are very prominent in the bay, especially the 'Paramoudra Flints', large masses up to 1 m length which appear to be original burrows expanded by overfilling with flint.

Return to the car park or take the coastal path back to Bridlington, or north to Speeton via the R.S.P.B. reserve at Bempton (TA 198742). *None of the coastal sections below Bempton cliffs should be visited even at low tide.*

Geology in Yorkshire's museums

Paul Ensom *Yorkshire Museum, York*

A HISTORICAL PERSPECTIVE

The earliest museums of Yorkshire developed during the 19th century at a time when geology, a new science, found itself in conflict with the accepted teaching of the Church on the Creation. Examples of early museums are the Leeds City Museum (1821) and Hull City, Whitby and the Yorkshire Museums (1823). Each was the product of a learned society based in an urban area. The collections of societies in Bradford and Sheffield also formed the basis of public museums. The Rotunda Museum (1829) in Scarborough is noteworthy, having been designed by (*the*) William Smith and Richard Sharp of York. William Smith spent his last years in North Yorkshire, and his nephew, John Phillips, who as his assistant received a sound geological education, became first Keeper of the Yorkshire Philosophical Society's museum and later Professor of Geology at Oxford. Many of Yorkshire's museums have their origins in the 20th century. The Tolson Museum in Huddersfield was a memorial to the two nephews of Legh Tolson who died in the First World War and the Craven Museum in Skipton (1928) grew from the Craven Museum and Archaeological Society.

What value museums?

Local museums are often the perfect entrée to the geology of an area. A better guide can seldom be had to what may be seen in the vicinity, thanks to generations of collectors – professional and amateur – all with an eye for the informative, the curious or the beautiful. Displays may elucidate the landscape's foundations and show the rock types, minerals and fossils likely to be encountered. Man's exploitation of coal, iron, lead and stone often figure in exhibits describing the social and economic history of the area. Archives, including photographs, add another dimension to the potential of these treasure houses.

The following list gives basic information about Yorkshire's geological museums, allowing the reader to assess what each one has to offer.

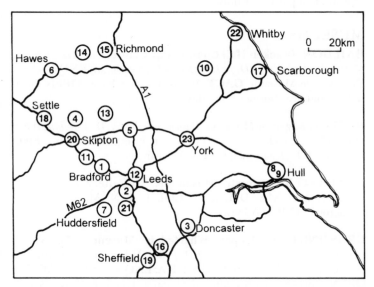

Figure 22 Location of museums of geological interest in Yorkshire.

Key to museum listings

D Displays: L=Local; R=Yorkshire; G=General geology.

TE Temporary exhibitions, ask museum for details.

COL Collections: L=Local; R=Yorkshire; N=UK; WW=world wide; m,r,f=minerals, rocks, fossils (M,R,F=particular strength); P, A & L=photographic, archive and library. Appointments should be made to examine collections, libraries, etc.

CAT Catalogues: Published catalogues of collections, histories of the collections, etc, which may be available for purchase.

ENQ Enquiry service: *=professional geologist on staff. Non-specialist staff & volunteers are often mines of information.

GACT Geological activities: Ask museum for details.

S Sales: Geological publications for sale.

AC Admission charge.

OPEN Fraught with problems! I have listed basic details only. As a rule all close on Christmas Day and Boxing Day and most if not all on New Year's Day. If you are travelling any distance to visit a particular museum it is always wise to phone to check opening times. Afternoon opening may be no more than 2 hours!

The absence of one of the above headings indicates that it is not relevant to a particular museum.

MUSEUMS

BAILDON: Bracken Hall Countryside Centre. *Glen Road, Baildon, Shipley, W. Yorkshire, BD17 5EA.* **D** L; **TE** Occasional; **ENQ** Yes* via Cliffe Castle Museum; **GACT** As advertised; **S** Basic; **OPEN** Open throughout year but not every day.

BATLEY: Bagshaw Museum. *Wilton Park, Batley, W. Yorkshire, WF17 0AS.* **TE** Yes; **COL** L & N, m (WW), r, F (esp.local Carb.); **ENQ** Basic; **GACT** Occasional; **OPEN** All year.

DONCASTER: Doncaster Museum & Art Gallery. *Chequer Road, Doncaster, DN1 2AE.* **D** L & G; **COL** L & N, M,r,f (esp. Carboniferous); **OPEN** All year.

GRASSINGTON: Upper Wharfedale Museum. *The Square, Grassington, Skipton, N.Yorkshire, BD23 5AQ.* **D** L industrial heritage – lead mining; **TE** Yes; **COL** L, M,R,f, P,A; **ENQ** Yes; **S** Basic; **AC** Yes; **OPEN** April–September afternoons daily, October–March Sat & Sun afternoons only.

HARROGATE: Royal Pump Room Museum. *Royal Parade, Harrogate, N.Yorkshire, HG1 2RY.* **D** L. Development of C19th Spa; **COL** L. m,r; **GACT** Sample the waters!; **AC** Yes; **OPEN** All year.

HAWES: Dales Countryside Museum. *Station Yard, Hawes, N.Yorkshire, DL8 3NT.* **D** L; **COL** L connected with lead mining; **CAT** Yes; **ENQ** Yes; **S** Local geology; **AC** Yes; **OPEN** Open April–October, occasionally in winter.

HUDDERSFIELD: Tolson Museum. *Ravensknowle Park, Wakefield Road, Huddersfield, W. Yorkshire, HD5 8DJ.* **TE** Yes; **COL** m(WW),r(L),f(L&N); **ENQ** Yes; **GACT** Yes; **S** Basic; **OPEN** All year.

HULL: Hull City Museums. *H.Q., 83 Alfred Gelder Street, Hull, HU1 1EP.* **D** In preparation; **TE** Yes; **COL** L & R. m,r,f,P,A; **CAT** Yes; **ENQ** Yes*; **GACT** Yes; **S** Yes; **OPEN** All year.

HULL: Yorkshire Water Museum. *Springhead Avenue, Willerby Road, Hull, HU5 5HZ.* **D** Development of water abstraction/pumping technology in E. Yorkshire; **COL** Rainfall records; **ENQ** Relating to water abstraction; **OPEN** Afternoons, closed Mondays and December.

HUTTON-LE-HOLE: Ryedale Folk Museum. *Hutton-le-Hole, N.Yorkshire, YO6 6UA.* **D** L. N.York Moors extractive industries; **ENQ** Basic; **S** Basic; **AC** Yes; **OPEN** Daily March–October.

KEIGHLEY: Cliffe Castle Museum, (Bradford Art Galleries & Museums). *Spring Gardens Lane, Keighley, W. Yorkshire, BD20 6LH.* **D** L. Economic geology of area & man's impact. Minerals; **TE** Yes; **COL** L & N. m,r,F (esp U. Carb. plants & Palaeozoic inverts); **CAT** Yes; **ENQ** Yes*; **GACT** Yes; **S** Basic books; **OPEN** All year, but closed Mondays except Bank Holidays.

LEEDS: Leeds City Museum. *Calverley Street, Leeds, W. Yorkshire, LS1 3AA.* **D** L & G; **COL** L, R & WW, m,r,f inc. Carb & Jur. plants; **ENQ** Yes*; **GACT** Yes; **S** Basic; **OPEN** All year, but closed Sunday and Monday.

PATELEY BRIDGE: Nidderdale Museum. *Council Offices, King Street, Pateley Bridge, N.Yorkshire, YO18 8DU.* **D** L. Special reference to quarrying & mining; **COL** L. m,r,f; **S** Local quarrying; **AC** Yes; **OPEN** Afternoons Easter–end September & winter Sundays.

REETH: Swaledale Folk Museum. *Reeth, N.Yorkshire.* **D** L. Lead mining, dressing & smelting. Lime production; **COL** Lead industry; **S** Local lead industry; **AC** Yes; **OPEN** Easter–end October.

RICHMOND: Richmondshire Museum. *Ryders Wynd, Richmond, N.Yorkshire, DL10 4JA.* **D** L. Mining; **COL** Minor collection. m,r; **ENQ** Basic; **AC** Yes; **OPEN** Easter–October.

ROTHERHAM: Rotherham Museum. *Clifton Park, Rotherham, S. Yorkshire, S65 2AA.* **D** G & L inc. economic geology – iron & coal; **COL** L. m,r,F; **ENQ** Basic; **S** Basic; **OPEN** All year, but closed Fridays & 25 Dec–1 Jan inclusive.

SCARBOROUGH: Wood End Museum of Natural History. *The Crescent, Scarborough, N.Yorkshire, YO11 2PW.* **D** L; **TE** Yes; **COL** L &

N. m & r(N),F(L); **ENQ** Yes; **S** Basic; **OPEN** All year Tues–Sat. Spring Bank Holiday–end September also open Sundays & Bank Holiday Mondays.

SETTLE: Museum of North Craven Life. *Chapel Street, Settle, N.Yorkshire, BD24 9HS.* **D** L inc. some bone cave material. Working model of Ebbing & Flowing Well of Giggleswick Scar; **COL** Display specimens only, r,f; **S** Basic local geology inc. local caves; **AC** Yes; **OPEN** Sat & Sun afternoons Easter–June and afternoons daily June–Sept.

SHEFFIELD: Sheffield City Museum. *Weston Park, Sheffield, S.Yorkshire, S10 2TP.* **D** L & G; **TE** Yes; **COL** L, N & WW. m,r,F esp. Coal Measure plants of S.Yorkshire; **CAT** Yes; **ENQ** Yes*; **GACT** Yes; **S** Basic; **OPEN** All year, but closed Mondays.

SKIPTON: Craven Museum. *Town Hall, High Street, Skipton, N.Yorkshire, BD23 1AH.* **D** L. m,f; **COL** L esp. Craven Reef Knoll fossils; **OPEN** Open throughout year except Tuesdays. Closed Sundays Oct–March.

WAKEFIELD, nr: Yorkshire Mining Museum. *Caphouse Colliery, New Road, Overton, nr Wakefield, W.Yorkshire, WF4 4RH.* **D** Coal mining history and technology; **COL** Items associated with mining industry, P,A,L; **ENQ** Yes*; **S** Basic; **AC** Yes; **OPEN** All year.

WHITBY: Whitby Museum. *Pannett Park, Whitby, N.Yorkshire, YO21 2AH.* **D** L including Zechstein evaporites & Whitby jet jewellery; **COL** L. m.F; **AC** Yes; **OPEN** All year.

YORK: Yorkshire Museum. *Museum Gardens, York, N.Yorkshire, YO1 2DR.* **D** R; **TE** Yes; **COL** L, R & N. m,r,F,L,P(WW volcanoes); **CAT** Yes; **ENQ** Yes*; **GACT** Yes; **S** Basic and more detailed; **AC** Yes; **OPEN** All year.

Acknowledgements

I would like to thank many museum colleagues in Yorkshire, John Nudds and the Geological Curators Group, and Jane Walton (Yorkshire and Humberside Museums Council) for providing the information used to compile this brief guide.

FURTHER INFORMATION

General

Museums Alive! is an annually produced guide to museums in Yorkshire and Humberside detailing admission charges, opening times, phone numbers, addresses etc. Copies available, free, from Yorkshire and Humberside Museums Council, Farnley Hall, Hall Lane, Leeds, LS12 5HA.

Collections and collectors

Hartley, M. M., Norris, A., Pettitt, C. W., Riley, T. H., & Stier, M. A. (1987) *Register of Natural Science Collections in Yorkshire and Humberside.* Area Museum and Art Gallery Service for Yorkshire and Humberside.

Nudds, J. R. (ed), *Directory of Geology Museums in the British Isles.* Geological Curators Group and Geological Society of London. Publication expected 1993. This will give substantially more details for some of the larger museums in the region.

Glossary

Acadian Orogeny *See* **orogeny.**

adit More-or-less horizontal tunnel to mine.

agate Variety of **quartz** with distinctive concentric colour banding.

alga (pl. algae) Primitive plant-like organism. Some may secrete calcium carbonate and algal mats may play a role in sediment accumulation in some environments. *See* **stromatolite.**

ammonite Extinct Mesozoic marine ammonoid **mollusc** (cephalopod), secreting a chambered shell of calcium carbonate, usually planispirally coiled (*See* **goniatite**).

anhydrite $CaSO_4$ White to grey, rock-forming **evaporite** mineral.

anticline *See* **fold.**

argillaceous Describing silt to clay-grade sediments (grains less than 0.0625 mm in diameter).

arkose Sand-grade rock containing 25% or more **feldspar.**

aurichalcite $(Zn,Cu)_5(CO_3)_2(OH)_6$ Bright turquoise-blue mineral in radiating aggregates of thin pearly crystals. A secondary mineral in oxidized zones of zinc and copper bearing **veins.**

azurite $Cu_3(CO_3)_2(OH)_2$ Deep azure blue mineral associated with the oxidized zone of copper deposits.

baryte/barytes $BaSO_4$ Baryte is a colourless to white mineral, crystals commonly tabular, noticeably heavy. A common **gangue** mineral. Barytes is the commercial product.

barytocalcite $BaCa(CO_3)_2$ Colourless to white or pale cream mineral.

basalt Dark, often almost black, fine-grained volcanic rock, low in silica (no **quartz**) and relatively rich in iron, magnesium and calcium.

belemnite Extinct **mollusc** (cephalopod). Internal skeleton consists of a solid calcium carbonate bullet-shaped 'guard' (part usually preserved), with chambered structure (phragmocone) in conical cavity at one end.

benthonic (benthic) Describing bottom-living organisms.

bioclastic Limestone composed of shells or skeletal fragments.

biostratigraphy Use of fossils to date and correlate rock sequences.

biostrome Sheet-like accumulation of fossil shells or skeletons.

bioturbation The destruction of primary structures (i.e. bedding) in an unconsolidated rock unit by burrowing organisms; hence **bioturbated.**

biozone Fundamental unit of **biostratigraphy.**

bivalve Marine to fresh-water **mollusc** in which the plane of symmetry of the bi-valved calcium carbonate shell is in the plane of opening of the two valves (as in cockles and mussels).

blastoid   Extinct Palaeozoic stalked **echinoderm** with a bud-like theca showing distinct pentameral symmetry.

bornite Cu_5FeS_2 (peacock ore) Reddish-brown to purplish-blue mineral, iridescent on tarnished surfaces; crystals often rough cubes.

brachiopod   Solitary marine animal with bi-valved calcite shell. The plane of symmetry is perpendicular to the plane of opening of the valves.

breccia   Coarse clastic rock in which the **clasts** are angular. *See* also **fault.**

bryozoa   Small colonial animal with a calcite skeleton consisting of large numbers of tiny tubular or box-like chambers. Colonial form very variable.

calcite $CaCO_3$ Colourless or white mineral which is the main constituent of limestone. Crystals when formed (i.e. in **veins**) may be tabular or prismatic.

Caledonian Orogeny   *See* **orogeny.**

carbonate rocks   Limestones or **dolostones** (**dolomites**).

carnelian   Reddish-white cryptocrystalline **quartz.**

chalcopyrite $CuFeS_2$ (copper pyrites) Brass-yellow mineral with an iridescent tarnish. Most common copper mineral. Crystals usually tetrahedra.

chalk   Very fine-grained, white to pale grey, carbonate rock principally formed of **coccolith** ooze. Characteristic of the European Upper Cretaceous.

chamosite (berthierine) $(Fe_5Al)(Si_3Al)O_{10}.(OH)_8$ Greenish-black mineral often found in sedimentary iron ores. Berthierine is the primary deposit which is converted to chamosite at moderate temperatures and pressures.

chert   Nodules, lenses or impersistent bands of cryptocrystalline **quartz**, usually black, grey or red in colour, usually of diagenetic origin in sedimentary sequences.

chronostratigraphy   Arrangement of rock sequences in terms of time.

cinnabar   HgS Most common mineral of mercury, scarlet to brownish red.

clast   Rock fragment; hence **clastic rock**. The principal clastic rocks are distinguished on grain size thus: **conglomerate** >2 mm $>$ sandstone $>$ 0.0625 mm $>$ siltstones $>$ 0.004 mm $>$ mudstone/shale. **Clast fabric** (imbrication) may indicate direction of water flow where platy/tabular casts lean in the direction of the current.

cleavage   A close-spaced, regular fracture or fabric imposed on strongly-**folded** beds and best developed in weaker, fine-grained rocks.

coccolith   Minute calcium carbonate plate or disc, usually less than 0.02 mm in diameter, part of the covering of a microscopic marine, planktonic, unicellular alga. Coccolith ooze is a major component of **chalk.**

cone-in-cone   Fabric of adjacent sets of vertically nested cones, each about 3 cm or more in diameter, caused by precipitation of $CaCO_3$ under pressure in a mud-grade rock.

concretion   Spherical or ellipsoidal, resistant mass formed by local early cementation of the sediment.

conformable   Sequence of rocks in apparently continuous succession.

conglomerate   Coarse **clastic rock** in which the clasts are rounded. An **intraformational conglomerate** is one formed of locally derived clasts from a recently deposited source.

conodont   A microscopic phosphatic, tooth-like fossil, part of the jaw apparatus of an extinct group of primitive vertebrates. Very useful in **biostratigraphy.**

coprolite   Fossilised excreta.

coquina   A (lenticular) bed consisting principally of shells.

coral   A polyp or polyps (anemone-like) with a basal skeleton of calcium carbonate. Corals may be solitary or colonial, the latter varying from flat, tabular masses to clusters of branching tubes.

crinoid   (sea lilies; feather stars) **Echinoderm** with a plated cup bearing feeding arms, supported in sea lilies by a stalk. The disc-shaped ossicles or columnals of the stalk are a major constituent of Palaeozoic limestones, hence **crinoidal limestone.**

cross-stratification, cross bedding, cross-lamination   Sedimentary structure in which the migration of the slip face of ripples, dunes or bars produces a series of inclined laminae (**foresets**) between sub-horizontal bedding surfaces. Different types are: **planar**, when the laminae are flat; **trough**, when the laminae are scoop-shaped; and **hummocky**, when individual **sets** of cross-beds cut across each other, leaving hummocky bounding surfaces.

cyclothem   A sequence of beds, repeated again and again in vertical succession. Particularly notable in the Carboniferous.

dating, radiometric   Rocks are dated by using the fixed rate of decay of parent isotopes of various radioactive elements to daughter products. The resulting age may be quoted with the parent isotope used, as in '^{14}C yrs', etc.

diagenesis   The changes that take place in the conversion of a sediment to a rock.

diamicton   An unsorted sediment with a mixture of larger **clasts** and a mud-grade matrix. **Diamictite** is the resulting rock.

dip   The maximum angle of inclination of a planar surface, usually bedding. Measured in the vertical plane at right angles to the **strike.**

disconformity   A break in the succession where the beds above and below are parallel.

disharmonic   *See* **fold.**

dolomite $CaMg(CO_3)_2$ White, colourless, yellowish or brown mineral, in rhombic crystals with curved faces. Term also used for the characteristically brownish-yellow rock composed mainly of the mineral, but more correctly termed **dolostone.**

downthrow   *See* **throw.**

drift   Any superficial, unconsolidated sediments of the Quaternary.

drumlin   Smooth, streamlined, oval mound of **till** (boulder clay), usually in groups (drumlin field or swarm), formed beneath an advancing ice sheet. The long axis of the drumlin is parallel to the direction of advance.

dyke   More or less vertical, cross-cutting intrusion.

echinoderms   Marine invertebrates including **echinoids, crinoids, blastoids,** starfish and brittle stars. Characterized by a fundamental pentameral symmetry.

echinoid   (sea urchin) **Echinoderms** with body enclosed in a globular or discoidal test. Symmetry either pentameral radial (regular echinoids) or pentameral bilateral (irregular, burrowing, echinoids).

epicontinental   On continental crust, as in epicontinental sea.

epiplanktonic   Organism living in plankton by attachment to other planktonic organisms or floating objects.

erratic   Glacially transported rock derived from outside the local area.

esker   Long, sinuous, steep-sided ridge consisting of sands and gravels, formed either in an englacial tunnel or at the edge of a retreating ice sheet.

eustatic   World-wide change in sea level.

evaporite   Rock or mineral formed by precipitation of salts from natural brines by evaporation.

facies   Features of a rock or rock sequence that reflect the environment of deposition.

fault   A more or less planar fracture in a rock mass along which relative displacement of adjacent blocks has occurred. The **hade** is the inclination of the fault plane relative to the vertical. The face of the block above an inclined fault plane is the **hanging wall**, that below is the **footwall.** In most faults the direction of movement is known or assumed to be predominantly vertical. In a **strike-slip** or **wrench** fault, the direction of movement is predominantly horizontal. A **thrust** fault has a subhorizontal plane of displacement. Fractured rock on the fault plane caused by movement between adjacent blocks is a fault **breccia.**

feldspars   Important group of rock-forming silicate minerals, common in igneous rocks and usually broken down quickly on weathering. Hence **feldspathic.**

fireclay   *See* **seatearth.**

flat   A lenticular zone of mineralization parallel to bedding.

flint   A variety of cryptocrystalline **quartz** commonly present as grey or grey/black nodules and bands in **chalk.** It probably formed as a gel from organic silica (**sponge** spicules), and may fill or replace fossil tests, shells and burrows.

fluorite CaF_2 Colourless to translucent yellow, green, blue or purple, more rarely red or black mineral commonly crystallizing in cubes. **Fluorspar** is the commercial product.

flute cast (flute mark)   *See* **sole structure.**

fold   A bend in bedded rocks or any planar rock mass. An **anticline** is arched upwards with older rocks in the core. A **syncline** is bent downwards with younger rocks in the core. An **isoclinal fold** has subparallel fold limbs. The dip of the fold axis is the **plunge** of the fold. Folds are **disharmonic** when they change shape and/or size when traced into adjacent beds.

footwall *See* **fault.**

foraminifera Microscopic single-celled organism with a chambered, usually calcium carbonate, test.

foresets *See* **cross-stratification.**

galena PbS Lead-grey mineral crystallizing in cubes and octahedra.

gangue Bulk mineral in **veins,** formerly of no commercial importance, with which ore minerals are associated (i.e. **quartz, fluorite, baryte**).

ganister *See* **seatearth.**

garnet Silicate mineral of variable composition, often deep reddish-brown in colour, found in **igneous** and **metamorphic** rocks.

gastropod **Mollusc** with a usually helically coiled calcium carbonate shell (snail) or naked (slug).

gelifluctate Rock material derived from flow of water-saturated sheets of rock debris over perennially frozen ground (cold climate variety of **solifluction**).

glaciofluvial Sediments or landforms produced by meltwater from a glacier.

glauconite Silicate clay mineral, characteristically green, formed in some marine sediments.

gneiss Coarse-grained, banded rock formed under high-grade **metamorphic** conditions.

goniatite Palaeozoic ammonoid. Goniatites are the direct ancestors of the **ammonites.**

graben A linear tract of country, lowered between two bounding **faults.** A **half-graben** is fault-bounded on one side only.

graptolite Extinct group of marine, pelagic, colonial organisms with an organic skeleton.

gypsum $CaSO_4.2H_2O$ **Evaporite** mineral, usually white, as tabular crystals or massive. A transparent variety (**selenite**) may be precipitated within sediments under some conditions.

gyttja Rapidly accumulated organic-rich muddy deposit.

hade *See* **fault.**

half-graben *See* **graben.**

halite (rock salt) NaCl Common salt, an evaporite mineral, usually white; crystals usually cubes.

hanging wall *See* **fault.**

hemimorphite (calamine) $Zn_4(Si_2O_7)(OH)_2.H_2O$ White, grey, green-brown or pale blue ore of zinc, small tabular crystals but normally radial or earthy masses.

hummocky cross-stratification *See* **cross-stratification.**

igneous Rocks crystallized or solidified from a molten state.

inlier   Area of older rocks surrounded by younger rocks.

intermontane basin   Sedimentary basin being infilled from erosion of surrounding mountains.

interstadial   A period of increased warmth or retreating ice between **stadials.**

intraclast   Carbonate fragment derived from the erosion of a nearby sediment and redeposited within the same area.

joint   Fracture in rock, usually occurring in more or less regularly spaced sets, along which little or no movement can be detected.

kame   Steep-sided mound of bedded glaciofluvial sand and gravel associated with stagnant ice. A **kame terrace** is a continuous linear feature formed between an ice mass and a valley wall. Subsequent ice melt may result in signs of marginal slumping.

kettle hole   Depression in glacial drift, possibly containing a lake, left by the melting of an included mass of ice.

lacustrine   Sediments or processes associated with lakes.

laterite   Crust of mainly hydrated iron and aluminium silicates produced by the weathering of certain rocks in tropical, humid conditions.

limonite $FeO(OH).nH_2O$ Yellowish-brown earthy mineral derived from the weathering of iron minerals in rocks.

lithology   Physical features of a rock. Hence **lithostratigraphy**, the stratigraphic ordering of different rock types.

loess   Unconsolidated, wind-deposited, mainly silt-grade sediment.

Ma   Abbreviation for 'million years'.

magma   A hot, liquid or semi-liquid melt within the Earth's crust; the source for all **igneous** rocks and processes.

malachite $Cu_2CO_3(OH)_2$ Bright green mineral usually found in banded spheroidal aggregates. A common secondary mineral in oxidized zone of copper deposits.

marcasite FeS_2 Pale bronze-yellow mineral, often occurring in spherical masses of radiating crystals in **chalk.**

marl   A calcareous clay with 35–65% soft calcium carbonate.

meltwater channel   Channel cut by the action of meltwater from a glacier or snow. Usually unrelated to the present drainage pattern.

mesothem   An approximately 5 **Ma** cycle of **eustatic** rise and fall of sea level. In the Carboniferous, many **cyclothems** may form sequentially within a mesothem.

metamorphic   Rock formed by the alteration of a pre-existing rock by changes in temperature and/or pressure.

mica   One of a group of silicate minerals characterized by a platy habit.

microfossil   Any fossil too small to be studied without a microscope.

mineral veins   *See* **veins.**

mollusc   One of a very diverse invertebrate group including the **bivalves**, **gastropods**, cephalopods (**ammonites**, **goniatites**, **belemnites** and **orthocones**) and **scaphopods**.

moraine An unsorted deposit of rock debris associated with the actions of a glacier.

nannofossil Extremely small fossil derived from nannoplankton, generally less than 0.05 mm in size, for example a **coccolith.**

non-sequence Any (usually) minor break in the rock sequence.

nunatak Rocky summit standing above a surrounding ice sheet during glaciation.

oncolite Spherical or sub-spherical particle, up to 50 mm in diameter, formed by the action of **algae** in trapping sediment on the surface of a mobile grain.

onlap *See* **overlap.**

ooid (oolith) Spherical to sub-spherical particle, less than 2 mm in diameter, formed by the concentric deposition of rings of (usually) calcium carbonate around a mobile grain.

oolite Rock formed largely of **ooids**. Characteristic of high-energy, shallow-water environments.

orogeny Process of mountain building by the lateral compression of thick rock sequences. The **Caledonian Orogenic Cycle** refers to a series of orogenic events in the Lower Palaeozoic of which the **Acadian Orogeny** (Lower Devonian) was the last. The **Variscan Orogeny**, whose main effects are seen in southwest England and Central Europe, spanned the late Devonian to late Carboniferous.

orthocone Extinct cephalopod **mollusc** with a straight, tapering, chambered shell.

outlier Area of younger rocks surrounded by older rocks.

overflow channel, spillway Channel carved by the overflow from an ice-dammed lake. Usually unrelated to the present drainage pattern.

overlap Relationship where successive beds of rock deposited by a transgression extend further than the one below, to rest in turn on (**onlap**) the surface of unconformity.

overstep Relationship where a bed deposited by a **transgression** rests on the eroded ends of several beds below the plane of **unconformity.**

paraglacial Subaerial processes acting on sediments and landforms produced by glaciation.

pelagic Organisms living in the body of the water, either floating (planktonic) or swimming (nektonic).

piedmont Tract of country at the foot of a mountain range.

pisolith Spherical to sub-spherical inorganic carbonate particle characterized by internal concentric lamination, usually several mm in diameter.

plate A part of the Earth's rigid outer shell (lithosphere), internally relatively free of earthquakes and volcanic activity but bounded by more or less continuous zones of earthquakes and volcanoes where the plates move against each other. **Plate tectonics** describes the processes and effects of plate motions and interactions.

plunge   *See* **fold.**
pluton   A large **igneous** intrusion.
progradation   The outward extension of a sedimentary deposit, such as a delta building out from a shoreline.
pyrite FeS_2 (fools gold) Common pale brass-yellow mineral, often crystallizing in cubes.
pyromorphite $Pb_5(PO_4)_3Cl$ Green, yellow or brown mineral, often with hollow prismatic or barrel-shaped crystals. A secondary mineral occurring in the oxidized zones of lead deposits.
quartz SiO_2 Very common mineral, usually transparent or white but may be variously coloured. Occurs in many **igneous** and **metamorphic** rocks, is the main constituent of sandstones and siltstones and a common **gangue** mineral in **veins.**
regression   Withdrawal of the sea from the land area due to a relative fall in sea level.
rock-salt   *See* **halite.**
scaphopod   Marine **mollusc** with a tusk-shaped hollow shell.
seatearth   A fossil soil with root traces found immediately below a coal seam. A **fireclay** is a pure clay seatearth, whilst a **ganister** is a pure quartz sand seatearth.
selenite   *See* **gypsum.**
septarian   Nodules or concretions with a series of internal mineral-filled (usually **calcite**) cracks.
siderite $FeCO_3$ Grey to grey-brown mineral widespread in certain sedimentary rocks, particularly sedimentary ironstone deposits and Coal Measures sequences.
siliciclastic   **Clastic** rocks formed predominantly of **quartz**, other silicate minerals and rock fragments.
sill   A tabular igneous intrusion, mainly concordant with bedding, although it may cut across beds from one level to another.
slickensides   A lineation on a **fault** or bedding plane caused by the relative movement of rock masses on either side. The surface is often coated by fibrous crystals, usually of **quartz** or **calcite**, aligned in the direction of movement.
smithsonite (calamine) $ZnCO_3$ Grey, brown or greyish-white mineral, usually occurring as spherical aggregations or stalactitic masses.
sole structure   Sedimentary structure cut into an underlying mudstone by a turbidity current and infilled by the overlying **turbidite** bed. Preserved as a cast on the base of the turbidite. **Flute cast (mark):** ovoid scoop-shaped structure caused by turbulent water flow, preserved as a lobe on the base of the turbidite.
solifluction   Downhill movement of surface layer of unconsolidated weathered material when saturated by water.
sphalerite (blende) ZnS Commonly a brown or black mineral with a resinous lustre and variable form. Most common ore for zinc.
spillway   General term for **meltwater** or **overflow channels.**

sponge   Primitive invertebrates with an often asymmetrical body supported by spongin and/or siliceous or calcareous spicules.

S.S.S.I.   Site of Special Scientific Interest.

stadial   A period of increased cold or advancing ice.

strike   Intersection of a bedding plane, or other planar surface, with the horizontal.

strike-slip   *See* **fault.**

stromatolite   A carbonate rock with a fine horizontal, domal or columnar banding, reflecting the control of deposition by an **algal** mat or microbial community living on the surface of the sediment.

strontionite $SrCO_3$ White to pale green, grey or pale yellow mineral, usually with prismatic or needle-like crystals.

stylolite   An irregular, suture-like contact, most common in limestones, produced by solution of the rock under high pressure.

subduction   The process whereby oceanic crust descends into the interior of the Earth beneath oceanic or continental crust at a convergent **plate** margin.

syncline   *See* **fold.**

tectonic   Caused by deformation of rock masses, as in mountain-building episodes.

tholeiitic basalt   A type of **basalt** oversaturated in silica, so that small amounts of **quartz** are present.

throw   Description of vertical component of movement on a **fault** plane. **Downthrow** emphasises the relative downward displacement of a block on one side of the fault, **upthrow** (less commonly used) emphasizes the relative upward displacement of a block.

thrust   *See* **fault.**

till (boulder clay)   Collective term for the group of unsorted sediments laid down by direct action of ice.

trace fossil   A structure, such as a burrow or a grazing trail, resulting from the activity of an animal.

transgression   An advance of the sea over the land, caused by a relative rise in sea level.

tufa   Rock formed by the deposition of calcium carbonate (more rarely silica) as a sometime porous and/or banded mass around saline springs, or associated with stalactites and stalagmites.

turbidite   Rock deposited from a turbidity current, a fast-flowing current charged with a high sediment load, initiated by the disturbance of soft sediment on a slope. A turbidite is poorly sorted but may show grading and **sole structures** on its base.

unconformity   Surface of contact between two groups of rocks resulting from the tilting or folding and erosion of the lower group (often in an **orogenic** event) before the deposition of the upper group.

Variscan Orogeny   *See* **orogeny.**

vein   A fracture, usually sub-vertical, which is mineralized, often with **quartz** or **calcite. A mineral vein** implies the presence of ore minerals.

witherite $BaCO_3$ A white or grey mineral, crystals six-sided prisms and pyramids. Notably heavy.

Yoredale   Name applied to repeat cycles of limestone-shale-sandstone(-seatearth-coal) (**cyclothems**) in the Carboniferous (Dinantian, early Namurian), derived from the old name for Wensleydale, where they are typically developed.

Bibliography

General

Boardman, J. (ed.) 1985. *Field Guide to the Periglacial landforms of northern England*. 82pp. Quaternary Research Association, Cambridge.

Ellis, S. (ed.) 1987. *East Yorkshire Field Guide*. vi+116pp. Quaternary Research Association, Cambridge.

Hemingway, J. E., Wilson, V. & Wright, C. W. 1968. *Geology of the Yorkshire coast*. Guide No. 34. 47pp. The Geologists' Association.

Kent, P. E. 1980. *Eastern England from the Tees to The Wash*. British Regional Geology. 2nd edn, vii+155pp. HMSO, London.

Rawson, P. F. & Wright, J. K. (eds) 1992. *The Yorkshire Coast*. Geologists' Association Guide No.34. 2nd edn, 117pp. PSS Group, Ongar.

Rayner, D. E. & Hemingway, J. E. (eds) 1974. *The geology and mineral resources of Yorkshire*. ix+405pp. Yorkshire Geological Society.

Reference works

Allaby, A. & Allaby, M. 1990. *The Concise Oxford Dictionary of Earth Sciences*. xxi+410pp. OUP, Oxford.

British Museum (Natural History) 1975. *British Palaeozoic Fossils*. 4th edn. 203pp. London.

British Museum (Natural History) 1975. *British Caenozoic Fossils*. 5th edn. 132pp. London.

British Museum (Natural History) 1983. *British Mesozoic Fossils*. 6th edn. 209pp. London.

Hamilton, W. R., Woolley, A. R. & Bishop, A. C. 1992. *Minerals, rocks and fossils*. 320pp. Hamlyn, London.

Roberts, J. L. 1989. *Field guide to geological structures*. 250pp. Macmillan, London.

Schumann, W. 1985 (1992). *Rocks, minerals and gemstones*. 380pp. HarperCollins, London.

Specific

Only works quoted in the text are listed here. Further articles on various aspects of the geology and geomorphology of Yorkshire may be found particularly in the *Proceedings of the Yorkshire Geological Society* as well as in many other journals, British Geological Survey Memoirs, and Geologists' Association guides.

Arthurton, R. S., Johnson, E. W. & Mundy, D. J. C. 1988. Geology of the country around Settle. *Memoir of the British Geological Survey*, Sheet 60 (England and Wales), ix+147pp. HMSO, London.

Boardman J. (ed.) 1981. *Field Guide to eastern Cumbria*. 128pp. Quaternary Research Association, London.

Bristow, C. S. & Best, J. M. (eds) 1993. *Braided Rivers: Form and Processes*. Geological Society Special Publication.

Chisholm, J. I. 1981. Growth faulting in the Almscliff Grit (Namurian E1) near Harrogate, Yorkshire. *Transactions of the Leeds Geological Association*, **9**, 5, 61–70.

Cooper, A. H. & Burgess, I. C. in press. Geology of the country around Harrogate. *Memoir of the British Geological Survey*, Sheet 62 (England and Wales). HMSO, London.

Cope, J. C. W., Ingham, J. K. & Rawson, P. F. (eds) 1992. *Atlas of palaeogeography and lithofacies*. Geological Society Memoir No. 13, 153pp, 106 maps.

de Boer G., Neale, J. W. & Penny, L. F. 1958. A guide to the geology of the area between Market Weighton and the Humber. *Proceedings of the Yorkshire Geological Society*, **31**, 157–209.

Dunham, K. C. & Wilson, A. A. 1985. Geology of the Northern Pennine Orefield. Vol. 2. Stainmore to Craven. *Economic Memoir of the British Geological Survey*, 247pp. HMSO, London.

Ehlers, J. Gibbard, P. L. & Rose, J. (eds) 1991. *Glacial Deposits in Great Britain and Ireland*. 580pp. Balkema, Rotterdam.

Howarth, M. K. 1962. The Jet Rock Series and the Alum Shale Series of the Yorkshire Coast. *Proceedings of the Yorkshire Geological Society*, **33**, 381–422.

Lewis, D. (ed) 1991. *The Yorkshire Coast*. Normandy Press, Beverley, N. Humberside.

Milsom, J. & Rawson, P. F. 1989. The Peak Trough – a major control on the geology of the North Yorkshire coast. *Geological Magazine*, **126**, 699–705.

Pounder, E. J. 1989. *Classic Landforms of the Northern Dales*. 28pp. Geographical Association, Sheffield.

Bibliography

Raistrick, A. 1975. *The lead industry of Wensleydale and Swaledale*. Vol. 1. The Mines. 120pp. Moorland Publishing Co. Ltd., Ashbourne, Derbyshire.

Rose, J. 1980. Landform development around Kisdon, upper Swaledale, Yorkshire. *Proceedings of the Yorkshire Geological Society*, **43**, 201–219.

Rose, J. 1985. The Dimlington Stadial/Dimlington Chronozone: a proposal for naming the main glacial event of the Late Devensian in Britain. *Boreas*, **14**, 225–230.

Rose, J. & Mitchell, W. A. 1989. Quaternary geology of upper Swaledale and adjoining regions: field meeting report. *Mercian Geologist*, **11**, 275–283.

Scotese, C. R. & McKerrow, W. S. 1990. Revised World maps and introduction. *In* McKerrow, W. S. & Scotese, C. R. (eds) *Palaeozoic palaeogeography and biogeography*. Geological Society Memoir No. 12, 1–21.

Whitham, F. 1991. The stratigraphy of the Upper Cretaceous Ferriby, Welton and Burnham formations north of the Humber, northeast England. *Proceedings of the Yorkshire Geological Society*, **48**, 227–254.

Whyte, M. A. & Romano, M., 1993. Footprints of a sauropod dinosaur from the middle Jurassic of Yorkshire. *Proceedings of the Geologists' Association*, **104**, 195–199.

Wright, C. W. & Wright, E. V. 1942. The Chalk of the Yorkshire Wolds. *Proceedings of the Geologists' Association*. **53**, 112–127.

Wright, J. K. 1968. The Stratigraphy of the Callovian Rocks between Newtondale and the Scarborough Coast, Yorkshire. *Proceedings of the Geologists' Association*, **79**, 363–399.

Young, B. 1987. Uncommon Pennine Minerals. Part 1. Aurichalcite in the Yorkshire and Cumbria Pennines. Part 2. Strontianite from the Yorkshire Pennines. *Transactions of the Leeds Geological Association*, **11** (2–3), 25–40.

Index

Aalenian, 118, 173
Acadian, 26
Acadian Orogeny, 11, 23
Acanthocladia, 137
Acanthopleuroceras, 170
Ackworth Rock, 139
Acroteuthis, 189
Addlethorpe Grit, 126, 131
adit, 54
Aegocrioceras, 189
agate, 199
Airehead Springs, 34
Albian Stage, 143, 146, 190
alga, 74, 130, 137, 140, 141
  algae, 37
  algal limestone, 14
alluvial, 93, 123
  alluvial flat, 24, 122
alluvium, 123
Almscliff Crag, 76–82
Almscliff Grit, 177, 79, 80, 82, 83
Alston Block, 14
alum, 18, 116, 152, 164
Alum Shale Member, 113, 116, 118, 151, 152, 157, 159, 161, 162, 163, 172, 173
Amaltheus, 114, 155, 172
  A. stokesi, 172
ammonite, 17, 18, 19, 114, 143, 145, 146, 151, 154, 155, 156, 157, 161, 162, 163, 169, 170, 171, 172, 173, 177, 188, 189, 190, 196
Androgynoceras, 114, 170
Angram Reservoir, 65
anhydrite, 16, 133
Anthracoceras paucilobum, 64
anticline, 24, 25, 28
Apoderoceras, 170
Aptian Stage, 190
Arcow Formation, 28, 29
Arenig, 11, 23, 24
Arnioceras, 169
Arundian Stage, 41
Asbian Stage, 71, 72, 74
Ashgill, 11, 23, 24, 26, 27
Askrigg Block, 14, 15, 21, 23, 24, 27, 30, 31, 32, 58, 73, 75, 77
Atlantic Period, 123
aurichalcite, 56
Austwick Formation, 23, 27, 28
Avalonia, 9, 11, 23, 24
Avicula Seam, 151, 155
azurite, 36

bacteria, 71
Bakevellia, 136, 138, 139
Baltica, 9, 11, 23
Barden Syncline, 67
Barremian Stage, 189, 190
baryte, 16, 36, 37, 54, 55, 56, 57, 86
barytes, 55
barytocalcite, 57
basalt, 123
  basalt, tholeiitic, 19, 111, 114
Basement Till, 188, 196
belemnite, 18, 114, 143, 145, 146, 147, 154, 155, 157, 161, 162, 164, 169, 170, 171, 172, 177, 178, 180, 189, 190, 197, 198, 199
Belemnocamax boweri, 147
bentonite, 29
Berriasian Stage, 189
berthierine, 162
  berthierinitic, 177
biostrome, 37
bioturbated, 96, 169, 170, 180, 181
  bioturbation, 29
bivalve, 17, 18, 19, 64, 65, 86, 88, 89, 95, 100, 102, 114, 130, 136, 138, 139, 143, 146, 148, 149, 151, 154, 155, 156, 157, 161, 162, 169, 170, 172, 173, 177, 180, 181, 187, 188, 189, 191, 194, 199
Black Band, 147
blastoid, 63
block glide, 43, 46
Bolton Abbey, 66, 67
bone, 188, 189
  bone bed, 39
bornite, 16
Bositra radiata, 157
Boulby, 47
Boulby potash mine, 154
boulder bed, 27, 41, 47
  boulders, 48, 49
Bowland Shale, 31, 35, 37, 38, 39, 40, 41, 67, 69, 70, 71, 72, 74
brachiopod, 15, 18, 19, 27, 34, 37, 39, 61, 63, 64, 65, 74, 102, 109, 114, 145, 146, 147, 148, 155, 156, 170, 189, 190, 196, 197, 199
Bradgate Brickyard, 107
breccia, 16
  breccia, fault, 198
Brigantian Stage, 37, 60, 74

Brimham Rocks, 60
brittle star, 114
Bronze Age, 113
Brotherton Formation, 126, 130, 136, 139, 140
brown bear, 39
bryozoa, 16, 34, 61, 65, 137, 138, 139, 181
Burbage Edge, 104–7
Burnham Chalk Formation, 143, 148, 149, 198
burrow, 162, 177, 181, 199

Cadeby Formation, 125, 126, 128, 129, 130, 131, 132, 134, 136, 138, 139, 140
calamine, 35, 36
Calamites, 88, 100
Calcareous Shales, 169
Calcinema, 140
  C. permiana, 130
calcite, 39, 55, 57, 161, 175, 178, 191, 198
calcrete, 194
Caledonian Orogeny, 11
Callovian Stage, 175
cambering, 65
Camerogalerus cylindricus, 146
Caneyella membranacea, 64
cannel coal, 90
Caradoc, 11, 23
carbonate, 23, 36
Carbonicola communis non-marine bivalve Biozone, 100
Carboniferous, 11, 14, 15, 16, 21, 23, 25, 26, 27, 28, 29, 30, 51, 58–65, 66–75, 76–83, 84–91, 92–100, 101–9, 124, 125, 129, 131, 133
Cardium edule, 187
Carstone, 143, 145, 146
cave, 20, 35, 39, 61, 62, 129, 199
  cave earth, 39
  cavern, collapsed 73
Cayton Bay, 174
Cayton Clay Formation, 175, 177
Cementstone Beds, 190
Cenomanian Stage, 143, 145, 146, 147, 190
chalcopyrite, 16
chalk, 17, 19, 143, 145, 148, 149, 184, 185, 187, 190, 191, 192–9
chalybeate, 83
chamosite, 152, 156, 162

Index

chamositic, 171, 177
Chapel le Dale, 24
chert, 120
Chondrites, 156, 169, 170
cinnabar, 56
cist burial chamber, 117
clapper bridge, 28
clast fabric, 47
clastic, 23
  clastic rock, 11
  clastic sediment, 15
clay, 18, 20, 39, 111, 117, 120, 122, 123, 145, 175, 182, 184, 185, 188, 189, 190
  clay, dolomitic, 136
Clay Cross Marine Band, 109
Cleveland Basin, 17, 151, 168
Cleveland Dyke, 19, 111, 113, 115
Cleveland Hills, 19, 110–18, 119–23
Cleveland Ironstone Formation, 111, 113, 115, 116, 151, 154, 155, 173
Clitheroe, 14
Cliviger Fault, 86, 88
Cliviger Valley, 84–91
coal, 14, 15, 18, 36, 54, 65, 85, 89, 95, 100, 102, 107, 117
Coal Measures, 15, 24, 85, 88, 89, 95, 101, 102, 107, 134, 139
cobble bed, 47
  cobbles, 49
coccolith, 19
Cockhill Marine Band, 64
Colsterdale Limestone, 64
Colsterdale Marine Beds, 64
Compound Nodular bed, 189
Concinnithyris, 148
  C. concinna, 147
concretion, 17, 69, 86, 89, 90, 115, 154, 157, 161, 164, 170, 171, 173, 177, 181, 188
cone-in-cone, 162
conglomerate, 11, 14, 23, 26, 27, 37, 41, 64, 82, 115, 132, 156, 194
Coniacian Stage, 143, 149
conodont, 90
copper, 35, 36, 52
  copper mine, 33
coprolite, 188
Coprolite Bed, 184, 188
coquina, 134, 136, 154
coral, 15, 18, 34, 37, 62, 64, 65, 74, 148, 197
Cornbrash Limestone Formation, 175, 177, 178
cornelian, 199
Cove Limestone Member, 32, 34, 37, 39
Craven Basin, 14, 15, 23, 31, 32, 67, 77

Craven Faults, 11, 14, 21, 23, 24, 26, 30–41, 67, 75, 77
Craven Inliers, 14, 21–9
Cravenoceras cowlingense, 64
Cravenoceras cowlingense Marine Band, 77
Cravenoceratoides nitidus, 64
Cremnoceramus deformis, 149
  C. inconstans, 149
  C. schloenbachi, 149
Cretaceous, 17, 18, 19, 142–9, 183, 184, 188, 192–9
crinoid, 19, 34, 37, 61, 63, 64, 169, 197
Crinoid Grit Member, 122
Crummack Anticline, 27
Crummack Dale, 26
crustacea, 189
cyclothem, 85, 88

Dacryomya ovum, 161
Dactylioceras, 161, 172
  D. commune, 118
  D. tenuicostatum, 157
Danes Dyke Fault, 197
Danes Dyke Member, 197
debris flow, 43, 46, 47, 48
Deepdale Marls, 148
deltaic, 15, 18, 60, 77, 85, 93, 95, 98, 100, 102, 117, 173, 175
Dent Fault, 14
Dentalium, 171
  D. giganteum, 154
Devensian Stage, 19, 20, 32, 35, 42, 43, 46, 63, 111, 119, 122, 125, 145, 184, 185, 187, 188, 194
Devonian, 11, 23, 28
diamicton, 42, 47, 49
Didymotis? uermoesensis, 148
Dimlington Stadial, 42, 46, 111, 112, 119
Dimorphoceras, 64
Dinantian, 11, 14, 30, 31, 37, 38, 40, 42, 51, 60, 66, 67, 71, 72, 93
dinosaur footprints, 162
Diplocraterion, 169
disconformity, 14, 139
dissolution residue, 16
Dogger Formation, 118, 159, 161, 162, 173
dolomite, 14, 16, 126, 128, 129, 130, 131, 132, 133, 136, 137, 138, 139, 188
  dolomite, oolitic, 128
  dolostone, 40
Double Band, 168, 170
Draughton Limestone, 71
drift, 27, 72, 119, 123, 145, 194, 196, 198
  drift tail, 46
drumlin, 46, 120, 185, 187
Dunbarella papyracea, 89
dyke, 26, 111, 114

East Midlands Shelf, 17
Echinocorys, 148
  E. scutata, 149
echinoderm, 18
echinoid, 19, 146, 147, 148, 149, 189, 196, 197, 198, 199
Echioceras, 170
Edlington Formation, 126, 130, 131, 136, 140
Elland Flags, 95, 100
Ellerbeck Formation, 159, 161
Endemoceras, 189
Enthorpe Marls, 148
Entolium, 177
Epararietites, 169
Equisetites, 115
Equisetum, 180
erratic, 20, 27, 43, 49, 112, 115, 123, 168, 188, 194, 199
esker, 49, 120, 125
estuarine, 187
Eumorphoceras bisulcatum, 64
evaporite, 16, 17, 136, 140
Ewaldi Marl, 184, 190

faecal pellets, 197
feldspar, 29, 104, 114
  feldspathic, 60
fenestral fabric, 141
Ferriby Formation, 143, 146
Feruginous Flint, 199
Filey Bay, 183
fireclay, 95
fish, 64, 102, 164
Five Yard Limestone, 57, 61
flagstone, 29, 86
Flamborough Chalk Formation, 194, 197
Flamborough Head, 192
Flamborough Moraine, 194
Flamborough Sponge Bed, 196
Flandrian, 119
flat, 52
flint, 19, 143, 145, 148, 191, 194, 198, 199
fluorite, 16, 55, 56
fluorspar, 52
flute casts, 29
  flute mark, 64
fluvial, 98, 102, 107
  fluviatile, 15, 17, 18, 159, 175
foraminifera, 15

Gagaticeras, 169
Gainsborough Trough, 93
galena, 16, 35, 36, 37, 52, 54, 55, 56, 73, 86, 88
gangue, 55
  gangue mineral, 16
ganister, 54, 95, 131
Ganister Rock, 89
garnet, 199

Gastrioceras, 106
?*Gastrioceras*, 107
Gastrioceras cancellatum
   Marine Band, 91
Gastrioceras cumbriense
   Marine Band, 91
Gastrioceras listeri Marine
   Band, 89
Gastrioceras subcrenatum
   Marine Band, 88
gastropod, 149, 180, 187, 189
Gault Clay, 184, 190
Gayle Limestone, 37
gelifluction, 187
   gelifluctate, 19
geophysical, 23
Gervillia, 178
Gibbithyris semiglobosa, 148
Gigantoproductus, 37, 63
Girvanella Band, 37, 74
glacial, 17, 19, 20, 27, 71, 72,
   73, 81, 84, 113, 119, 122,
   125, 184, 196, 197, 198
   glacial diversion channel,
     131
   glacial drainage channel,
     115, 122
   glaciation, 21, 26, 42–50,
     63, 111, 188
   glacier, 188
glaciofluvial, 19, 43, 47, 111,
   120, 122, 123, 196
glauconite, 61, 189, 190
   glauconitic, 189
gneiss, 154
goniatite, 14, 15, 60, 64, 69,
   86, 88, 89, 91, 102
Goodmanham Channel, 145,
   148
Gordale Limestone Member,
   32, 33, 34, 35, 37, 39, 40
Gordale Scar, 32
granite, 11, 23, 31
graptolite, 11, 23, 29
Grassington Grit Formation,
   32, 35, 36, 61, 63, 67, 74,
   77
gravel, 20, 48, 49, 111, 120,
   122, 125, 145, 185, 187,
   194
Great Ayton, 110
Great Scar Limestone, 73
Greensand Streak, 190
Gresslya, 161
Grey Shale Member, 157,
   172, 173
greywacke, 145
Grimbald Crag Fault, 130
Gristhorpe Member, 175,
   180, 181
Gristhorpe Plant Bed, 180,
   181
grit, 61, 64, 65, 69, 70, 71, 72,
   74, 75, 77, 81, 83, 102,
   104, 106
Gryphaea, 169, 171, 177

Gunnerside, 51
gypsum, 16, 126, 136
gyttja, 43

Hackness Rock Member, 177
Hagenowia blackmorei 198
Halifax, 92
halite, 16, 17
Hampole Beds, 134, 140, 141
Hampole Discontinuity, 134,
   141
Haploecia straminea, 181
Hardraw Scar Limestone, 37
Harlow Car, 76, 82–3
Harpoceras, 164
   H. exaratum, 164
   H. falciferum, 157, 172
Harrogate Anticline, 77, 83,
   125, 131
Hauterivian Stage, 189
Hawes Limestone, 35, 36, 37,
   38, 39
Hawsker Bottoms, 165
Helweth Beck Member, 180
Hemiaster, 146
hemimorphite, 56
Hettangian Stage, 168
Hibolites jaculoides, 189
Hildoceras, 161, 172
hippopotamus, 39
Holaster subglobosus, 146
Holcombe Brook Grit, 90
Holderness, 19, 20, 142
Holkerian Stage, 41
Holocene, 42, 43, 46
Hooton Pagnell, 136, 137
Horton Formation, 28, 29
Howardian-Flamborough
   Fault System/Zone, 194,
   198
Huddersfield Basin, 93
human artifact, 196
Hunstanton Formation, 143,
   145, 146, 194
hush, 55, 56
hyaena, spotted, 39
Hydrobia ulvae, 187
hydrocarbon, 151, 157

Iapetus Ocean, 11, 23
ice sheet, 19, 20
ice-dammed lake, 46
ice-tongue hollow, 48
igneous, 19, 145
Ilfordian Interglacial, 188
Infulaster excentricus, 148
Ingleton, 24
Ingleton Group, 23, 24, 25, 26
inlier, 11, 34, 37, 60, 102, 106
Inoceramus, 191
   I. crippsi, 143, 146
   I. lamarcki, 149
   *I. lamarcki geinitzi – I. l.
     cuvieri* group, 148
interglacial, 20, 196

Ipswichian, 196
   Ipswichian Interglacial, 39
iron, 152
   iron ore, 113, 116
   iron oxides, 19, 28
Iron Age, 106, 113, 118, 197
ironstone, 17, 18, 100, 107,
   113, 115, 116, 118, 151,
   152, 154, 156, 161, 170,
   171, 172, 178, 181
Ironstone Shales, 114, 170,
   172
island arc, 23

jet, 18, 113, 115, 152, 154,
   157, 164
Joan Coal, 109
Jurassic, 17, 18, 110–18, 122,
   123, 142, 143, 146, 150–
   7, 158–64, 165–73, 174–
   82, 183, 187, 188, 194

kame, 43, 49
   kame terrace, 43, 46, 48
Keld, 42
kettle hole, 43
Kilnsey Formation, 34, 41
Kilnsey Limestone Member,
   34, 38
Kimmeridge Clay, 18, 188
Kimmerdigian Stage, 184
Kingsdale, 24
Kiplingcotes Flints, 148, 149
Kiplingcotes Marls, 148
Kisdon, 42–50
Knaresborough, 124

lacustrine, 111, 120
lake, 48, 49
   lake clay, 113
   lake deposits/sediments, 43,
     46, 47, 125
   lake peat, 43
Lake District, 23
Lake Humber, 145
Lake Scugdale, 122
landslide, 49
landslip, 35, 47, 49, 62, 63,
   65, 115, 123, 168, 173,
   178, 185, 189
Laurentia, 9, 11, 23
lead, 16, 35, 52, 54, 86
   lead mine, 46
Lebberston Member, 175,
   180, 181
Lias Group, 17, 113, 114, 115,
   116, 117, 118, 143, 146,
   151, 172, 173
Liassic, 111, 114, 115, 168
Libishaw Sandstone, 65
Lidgett Coal, 109
Liebea, 130, 136, 138, 140
liesegang rings, 28
limestone, 14, 15, 16, 17, 18,
   24, 26, 27, 29, 31, 33, 34,
   35, 36, 37, 38, 39, 40, 42,

52, 54, 60, 61, 62, 63, 64,
  67, 69, 71, 72, 73, 74, 93,
  126, 129, 130, 140, 164,
  171, 175, 177, 181, 190
limestone, cherty, 39
limestone, dolomitic, 126,
  130
limestone, oolitic, 14, 16
limestone, silicified, 35, 36
limestone pavement, 27, 34
Limley Anticline, 62
limonite, 67
Lingula, 65, 109
lion, 39
Liostrea, 114, 171
Lithostrotion, 37
Littorina littorea, 187
  L. rudis, 187
Llandeilo, 23
Llandovery, 11
Llanvirn, 11, 23, 24
loam, 187
Loch Lomond Stadial, 46
loess, 19, 120
Lopha, 177, 178
Lower Brimham Grit, 60
Lower Calcareous Grit
  Formation, 175, 177
Lower Follifoot Grit, 64, 125
Lower Haslingden Flags, 86,
  90, 95
Lower Magnesian Limestone,
  125
Lower Palaeozoic, 11, 21–9,
  31
Lower Pink Band, 146
Lower Plompton Grit, 125,
  130
Ludlow, 11, 23, 28, 29
Lyticoceras, 189

Macoma balthica, 187, 188
Magnesian Limestone, 133
Main Chert, 55, 56
Main Limestone, 40, 52, 54,
  56
Main Seam, 151, 155, 156
malachite, 36, 37
Malham, 30
Malham Cove, 34
Malham Formation, 31, 32,
  34, 35, 37, 38
Malham Tarn, 34
mammal, 20, 39
  mammalian bone, 196
mammoth teeth, 196
marcasite, 194
Market Weighton, 142
Market Weighton Block, 17,
  142, 146, 151, 194, 198
Market Weighton Granite, 11
Market Weighton Spillway,
  145
marl, 17, 19, 43, 143, 147,
  148, 194, 197, 199
Marsdenian Stage, 95, 102

Marsupites, 197
  M. testudinarius, 197
Meleagrinella, 180
meltwater channel, 32, 43, 46,
  47, 49, 50, 84, 111, 118,
  120
Mercia Mudstone, 17
Mesolithic, 113
mesothem, 14
Mesozoic, 19, 175, 185, 187
metamorphism, 24, 111, 114
Meyeria ornata, 189
mica, 104
Micklefield, 140
Micraster, 149
  M. corbovis, 148
Middle Limestone, 37, 61, 62,
  63
Middle Marl, 126
Midgley Grit, 95
Milankovitch cycles, 177
Millepore Bed, 175, 181
Millstone Grit, 15, 42, 58, 60,
  76–83, 85, 86, 93, 95,
  101, 102
millstones, 105
mine, 35, 74, 114, 116, 118,
  151, 156
Mineral Belt, North
  Swaledale, 51–7
mineral vein, 16, 73
mineralization, 24, 30
mineralized fault, 38, 73
mining, 47, 86
Mississippi Valley
  mineralization, 16
mollusc, 34, 180, 188
moraine, 71, 72, 120, 122,
  125, 145
Moutonithyris dutempleana, 145,
  146
mud, 134, 136, 151, 159
mudflow, 178, 196
mudstone, 11, 17, 23, 29, 31,
  36, 37, 39, 60, 61, 62, 64,
  65, 77, 80, 82, 107, 126,
  131, 156, 163
Muker, 42
Mulgrave Shale Member,
  113, 115, 151, 152, 157,
  159, 163, 164, 172
Mull, 19
museum, 61, 200–5
Mytilus edulis, 187

Namurian, 14, 15, 30, 35, 36,
  39, 40, 42, 51, 54, 60, 65,
  66, 67, 72, 74, 76, 84, 88,
  89, 93, 95, 102, 125
Neohibolites, 143
  N. minimus, 145, 146
  '*N. minimus*', 190
  N. ewaldi, 190
Neolithic, 39, 113
nickpoint, 48
Nidderdale, 58–65

Nidderdale Shale, 64, 65
Nissonia, 115
nodule, 65, 89, 96, 100, 106,
  107, 146, 162, 163, 169,
  171, 172, 189, 190, 191,
  194
nodule, calcareous, 29
non-sequence, 184
Norber Formation, 24, 26
North Sea, 18, 19
North Sea Basin, 17
North York Moors, 9, 111
Northern Pennine Orefield,
  52
nunatak, 48

oil, 18, 152, 157
Oistoceras figulinum, 171
oncolite, 37
ooid, 162
oolite, 125, 126, 128, 129, 134,
  136, 137, 139, 177
oolitic, 152, 171, 181
oolith, 137, 141, 156
Ophiomorpha, 169, 170
Orbirhynchia, 148, 149
Orbitremites, 63
Ordovician, 9, 11, 21, 23, 26
Orionastraea garwoodi var
  pristina, 62
Ornatothyris, 145
orthocone, 29
Osgodby Formation, 175, 177
outlier, 65, 111, 115, 126
outwash, 122
Ovaticeras ovatum, 163
Ovatum Band, 163
overflow channel, 145
Owd Bett's Marine Band, 90
Oxford Clay Formation, 18,
  175, 177, 178
Oxfordian, 175
Oxynoticeras, 169
Oxyteuthis, 189
Oxytoma cygnipes, 156
  O. inequivalvis, 154
oyster, 172, 199

palaeocliff, 26
palaeokarst, 39
paraglacial, 42, 46, 48
Paramoudra Flints, 199
*Parapuzosia (Austiniceras)
  austeni*, 145, 146
Parasmilia, 148
Pateley Bridge, 60
Peak Fault, 168
Peak Trough, 175
peat, 54, 120, 123
  peat, blanket, 43
pebble bed, 14, 17
Pectinitites pectinatus, 188
Pendle Grit Formation, 31,
  35, 36
Pendleian Stage, 39, 67, 69
Pendleside Limestone, 41

Pennine Basin, 15, 93
Pennines, 9, 16, 19, 20, 58, 84, 86, 92
Pentacrinites, 169, 170
periglacial, 19
Permian, 15, 16, 124–32, 133–41
Permophorus, 136
Pholadomya, 114, 156, 177, 181
phosphate, 188, 190
phosphatic, 189, 190
Pinna, 170, 178
pisolith, 137
plant, 115
  plant debris/fragments/material/remains, 96, 100, 102, 106, 107, 162, 178
plate tectonic, 23
Platypleuroceras, 170
Platythyris capillata, 146
Pleistocene, 21, 26, 39, 185
Plenus Marls, 147
plesiosaur, 189
Pleuromya, 169, 171
  P. costata, 156
Pliensbachian, 114, 151, 170, 171, 172
pollen, 46
Port Mulgrave, 150
Posidonia retusta, 64
potash, 16
Precambrian, 24
Protocardia, 114, 154, 156, 171
  P. truncata, 154, 172
Pseudolima, 114
Pseudomytiloides, 164
  P. dubius, 157
Pseudopecten, 114, 171
  P. equivalvis, 156
Pteroperna, 181
Ptilophyllum, 115
Pycnodonte vesicularis, 148
pyrite, 16, 71, 152, 157, 161, 164, 170, 172, 181, 189
  pyritic, 163, 171, 188, 189, 190
  pyritized, 178
Pyritous Shales, 170
pyromorphite, 56

quartz, 29, 35, 37, 60, 79, 83, 99, 104, 129, 130
Quaternary, 19, 30, 35, 42–50, 77, 110, 112, 118, 119–23, 168, 183, 184, 185

Ravendale Flints, 148, 199
Ravenscar Group, 111, 122, 159, 175
Rawtheyan Stage, 27
Rectithyris, 145
Red Chalk, 143, 184, 189, 190, 194
Red Cliff Fault, 175, 178

Red Scar Grit, 64, 65
Redcar Mudstone Formation, 114, 123, 169, 172
Redcliff Rock Member, 177, 178
reef, 14, 16, 18, 31, 33, 34, 35, 37, 38, 40, 134, 137, 138, 139
reptile, 18
Reticuloceras bilingue, 89
Reticuloceras bilingue Marine Band, 95
Reticuloceras metabilingue Marine Band, 95
Reticuloceras superbilingue Marine Band, 102
rhinoceros, narrow-nosed, 39
Rhizocorallium, 156, 169, 170, 177
Ribblesdale, 28
Richmond Chert, 56
Ringinglow Coal, 102
Rivelin (or Chatsworth) Grit, 102, 104, 105, 106, 107
river terrace, 47, 48, 70
Robin Hood's Bay, 165
rock-salt, 136
Roman, 106
Romano-British, 39
root system, 162
rootlet, 131, 180
Roseberry Topping, 110, 115
Roseberry Topping Plant Bed, 115
Rossendale Basin, 93, 95
Rossendale Ridge, 93
Rough Rock Flags, 95
Rough Rock Group, 86, 88, 91, 95, 96, 99
Roxby Formation, 130

saccolith, 137
Salenia granulosa, 148
Saltwick, 158
Saltwick Formation, 115, 117, 154, 157, 159, 161, 162, 164, 173
sand, 20, 47, 48, 111, 120, 122, 123, 125, 136, 145, 194
  sand, arkosic, 136
  sand, dune 16
sandstone, 11, 14, 15, 17, 18, 23, 24, 25, 26, 27, 28, 29, 32, 36, 42, 49, 57, 60, 61, 63, 64, 65, 77, 79, 80, 81, 83, 85, 86, 88, 89, 90, 93, 95, 96, 98, 99, 100, 102, 105, 106, 107, 111, 113, 114, 115, 116, 117, 118, 120, 122, 125, 126, 128, 129, 131, 132, 139, 154, 159, 162, 169, 171, 172, 173, 175, 177, 178, 181, 182
  sandstone, feldspathic, 65, 86, 99, 104, 129

Scalby Formation, 175, 177, 178, 180, 182
scaphopod, 154, 171
Scar House Formation, 63
Scar House Reservoir, 63
Scarborough Formation, 175, 178, 180, 181, 182
Schizodus, 136, 138, 139
  S. obscurus, 130
scree, 49
Scrobicularia piperata, 187
Scugdale, 119
Scugdale Moraine, 123
seatearth, 14, 65, 90, 95, 102, 107
selenitic, 189
Selwicks Bay Fault, 198
septarian, 171
Settle, 30
Sewerby Buried Cliff, 196
Sewerby Gravels, 196
Sewerby Member, 194
shake hole, 36
shale, 14, 17, 18, 35, 36, 42, 49, 67, 69, 71, 74, 85, 88, 89, 90, 93, 95, 99, 100, 102, 105, 106, 107, 109, 111, 114, 117, 118, 123, 125, 151, 152, 154, 156, 157, 159, 161, 164, 169, 170, 171, 172, 177, 178, 181, 184, 188
Shap Granite, 115, 123
Sheffield, 101
shell-bank, 136
shelly fauna, 29
Sherwood Sandstone, 17
siderite, 65, 86, 89, 106, 152, 154, 157, 161, 162, 177
  sideritic, 163, 171, 172
silica, 191
Siliceous Shales, 170
siliciclastic, 37
silt, 47, 111, 120, 123, 136, 145, 170
siltstone, 11, 17, 23, 24, 25, 26, 27, 28, 29, 39, 64, 77, 83, 85, 95, 96, 98, 99, 100, 106, 107, 114, 126, 131, 132, 154, 159, 162, 169, 171, 178
Silurian, 9, 11, 21, 23, 28, 145
Simbirskites, 189
Siphonodendron, 37
Skibeden Shale, 67, 71
Skipsea Till, 184, 185, 187, 188, 194, 196
Skipton Anticline, 67, 69, 71
Skipton Moor Grit, 67
Skyreholme Anticline, 67, 73, 74
slate, 25
slickensides, 198
slump fold, 25
slump-faulting, 80
Smelt Mill Sink, 34

Index

smithsonite, 35, 56
snakestone, 161
Sole Pit Trough, 151, 168
sole structure, 25, 29, 83
solifluction, 105
South Elmsall, 138
South Landing Member, 197
Speeton, 183
Speeton Clay, 184, 185, 187, 188
Speeton Shell Bed, 185, 187, 188
Speeton Shrimp, 189
speleothem, 39
sphalerite, 16, 36, 54, 56, 57, 157
spillway, 122, 123, 145, 197
Spirifer, 64
sponge, 19, 175, 191, 196, 198
spore, 17
Sprotbrough Member, 125, 128, 130, 134, 140
stack, 199
Stainmore Trough, 14, 15
Staithes, 150
Staithes Sandstone Formation, 111, 114, 151, 154, 171
starfish, 196, 197
Sternotaxis placenta, 148, 149
S. planus, 199
Stockdale Lane, 40
stromatolite, 16, 138
strontianite, 55, 56, 57
Studrigg-Studfold Syncline, 27, 28
stylolites, 197
subduction, 11, 23
subglacial, 47, 49, 50
Sugar Loaf Limestone, 39
Sugar Loaf Shales, 39
Swainby, 122
Swaledale, 42–50, 51–7
swallow hole, 74
Sycarham Member, 181
syncline, 25, 26, 28

Teesside, 19
Teichichnus, 169, 170
Ten Fathom Grit, 56
Terebratulina etheridgei, 147
Tertiary, 19, 93, 110, 113, 140, 194
Tethys Ocean, 17
Tetrarhynchia, 114, 172

T. tetrahedra, 156
Thalassinoides, 177
The Strid, 72
Thinfeldia, 115
Thornton Force, 25
Three Yard Limestone, 60, 61, 65
till, 20, 35, 39, 42, 43, 50, 52, 77, 81, 111, 113, 120, 122, 125, 145, 168, 175, 180, 184, 185, 188, 199
Toarcian Stage, 151
Todmorden, 84
Tornquist's Sea, 11
Totternhoe Stone, 145, 146
trace fossil, 154, 156, 169
Triassic, 17, 116
Trigonia, 177, 180, 181
trilobite, 27, 65
Triple Tabular Flints, 148
Trollers Gill, 66, 72
Tropidoceras, 170
tufa, 32, 33, 126
turbidite, 11, 23, 25, 27, 28, 29, 77, 83, 93
Turonian Stage, 148, 149

Uintacrinus socialis, 197
Ulceby Marl, 149
unconformity, 11, 16, 17, 18, 21, 23, 24, 26, 27, 28, 29, 39, 60, 125, 126, 128, 129, 130, 131, 133, 136, 143, 146, 151, 194
Underset Limestone, 54, 60
Unio, 162, 181
Unio Bed, 162, 164
Upper Bowland Shale, 36
Upper Follifoot Grit, 131, 132
Upper Haslingden Flags, 86, 95
Upper Magnesian Limestone, 126
Upper Marl, 130
Upper Plompton Grit, 128
Utriculus obtusus, 187

Valanginian Stage, 189
Vale of Pickering, 20
Vale of Mowbray, 17, 20
Vale of York, 17, 19, 20
Variscan, 67, 81
Variscan Orogeny, 15, 16, 93, 125
vein, 35, 36, 52–7, 198

vertebrate remains, 156
Victoria Cave, 39
Visean Stage, 31
volcanic, 23, 29
    volcanic ash, 189, 194
    volcanic clay, 29
    volcanic island arc, 11

Weberides barkei, 65
Welton Chalk Formation, 143, 148, 199
Wenlock, 11, 23, 26, 28, 29
Wensleydale, 14
Wensleydale Granite, 11, 14, 23
Wensleydale Group, 36, 37, 38, 39, 40
Westphalian, 15, 84, 88, 93
Wetherby Member, 125, 129, 134, 136, 138, 139, 140
Wharfedale, 66–75
Whet, 28
Whitby, 17, 158
Whitby Fault, 161
Whitby Mudstone Formation, 115, 116, 118, 151, 159, 172, 173
Whitby Plant Bed, 162
White Chalk, 184, 189, 190
Windermere Group, 26, 28
Windermere Interstadial, 46
witherite, 16, 55, 56
Withernsea Till, 184, 187
Wolstonian Stage, 188
wood, 18, 99, 152, 154, 156, 161, 170
Woodhead Hill Rock, 88
Woogill Coal, 64, 65

Yeadonian Stage, 95
Yellow Sands, 136
Yons Nab, 174
Yons Nab Beds, 175, 180, 181
Yoredale, 14, 36, 42, 60, 63, 64
Yorkshire Basin, 159, 173
Youngibelus, 164

Zamites, 115
Zechstein, 133
    Zechstein Basin, 134
    Zechstein Sea, 134, 136, 139
zinc, 35, 52